The Weibull Bible

Grasping Weibull Analysis for Engineers & Scientists

by Paul F. Watson

Published by Paul F. Watson

PO Box 102

Oceanside Oregon 97134

U.S.A.

To arrange for bulk purchase discounts for sales promotions, or educational purposes, contact the author at the above address. For information on translations and overseas distribution, please contact the author.

ISBN: 978-0-578-28061-5

Dedication
To Dr. Richard Price
Lamar University Mathematics Department
Who always gave the best to his students
And the community.

About This Book:

- This book and its cover were created using Affinity Publisher.

- Graphics processing & editing performed using Affinity Photo & Affinity Designer.

- Various commercially licensed fonts were used for graphics and text.

- Data analysis was performed using author developed Python programs.

  - Both Thonny and CodeRunner IDEs were used to develop Python programs

- Weibull-DR software was provided for evaluation by Applied Research Inc.

- The Watson-Weibull program is in development by the author.

- Equation creation/editing was by Math Cast, the open source equation editor.

About the Author:

Paul F. Watson holds degrees in Physics and Mechanical Engineering, both from Lamar University in Beaumont Texas. He spent 35+ years developing technical skills including statistical analysis. Over the years, he has been employed as engineer and teacher.

During most of his professional life, Mr. Watson was engaged in advanced aircraft design. His last ten years were spent as technical leader for an aircraft Integrity team responsible for approval of supplier reports including stress analysis, test plans, test reports and the integration thereof. The Integrity task necessitated a broad range of skills including engineering, statistics and computer programming.

Mr. Watson also spent six years overseas teaching both mathematics and English as a foreign language. Teacher and technical analyst combine in this introduction to Weibull Statistics with the following characteristics:

- An emphasis on communication rather than formality.

- An understanding of "points of confusion" likely to hinder a learner's progress.

- An understanding that students must leave with unquestioned capabilities.

Mr. Watson currently lives on the Oregon coast, continuing his research on statistical methods and going on country walks in the Great North-West.

Table of Contents:

Appendices:

Introduction: Another Book about Weibull?

Weibull Analysis is a powerful mathematical tool that can help professionals in many fields; yet, few understand what Weibull Analysis can do or how to use it. This book addresses these issues using college sophomore technical math.

I began my Weibull journey years ago when I needed to determine equipment life based on test data. I used Weibull; but, available literature was not adequate because a clear bridge was not established between data-theory and Weibull methods.

- Explanations were mired in unnecessarily complex mathematics.

- Some books provided detailed procedures but without explanation.

In writing The Weibull Bible, I created the needed book. The Weibull Bible replaces stilted explanations with informal clarity. Proofs utilizing advanced mathematics are replaced by data examples used to construct useful equations. The mistaken believe the Gaussian (Bell Curve) can explain most phenomena is replaced by examples of where it fails and Weibull succeeds.

Teaching techniques that stress "rigorous mathematical proof" are replaced by copious data examples that build concepts evolved into useful methods. Where needed, detailed technical demonstrations are banished to appendices with only brief explanations in the main text.

Prerequisites: The reader is assumed to have "rusty" knowledge of calculus and primitive knowledge of the Gaussian Distribution. Some knowledge of probability theory is helpful.

- It is not assumed the reader took calculus or statistics last week.

- Reviews of needed concepts are included in chapters else appendices.

- A scientific calculator and spreadsheet are essential.

- Note: Readers are unlikely to benefit without homework practice.

Chapter 1: Weibull Does as Data Is

A rather odd name for a chapter and a brief explanation is needed. John Berner at Applications Research commented, "What sets Weibull analysis apart is its unique ability to fit the Weibull equation through data-points as opposed to shoe horning an unwilling equation onto the data." After consideration, I realized John is right and my task is to explain what he meant.

A summary level Weibull analysis follows showing what "fitting the Weibull equation through data-points" means. This will be contrasted to a Gaussian Bell Curve analysis which

- Does not fit the Gauss equation through the data-points, and in consequence,

- Does not realistically represent the data-set.

Chapter 1 presents broad concepts. Only a general understanding is needed before moving on to following chapters which explain the "hows and whys" of doing actual analysis.

Historical Height of Tsunami Waves:

Figure 1-1: The Great 1928 Japan Tsunami (1)

Weibull analysis of Tsunamis was chosen to contrast Weibull success in fitting the equation through data-points versus Gaussian failure to describe data (2).

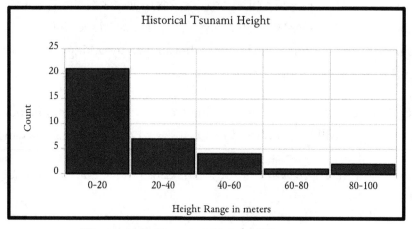

Figure 1-2: Tsunami Height Histogram

Example Weibull Analysis: (in three steps)

- Document the data (see Chapter 5 Homework Problem #7).

- Create a Weibull Plot based on pseudo data values and population percents.

- Use Weibull Plot to write Weibull Equation & Plot PDF similar to Figure 1-2.

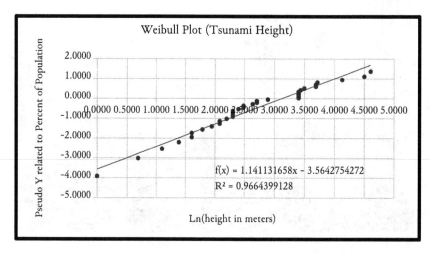

Figure 1-3: Weibull Plot of Tsunami Wave Heights

Figure 1-3 is a Weibull plot of data, based on pseudo x,y values explained in later chapters.

- The straight line on the Weibull Plot, is a representation of a Weibull Equation describing tsunami data. From the figure, it is evident that a straight line Weibull form has been forced through the points as described by Mr. Berner. It will be shown later that Gaussian analysis does not force equation through data and the omission results in a poor description of likely tsunami height.

- Weibull Plots are important. It may interest the reader that tightness of data-points to the line indicates how well Weibull can describe the data. For this data-set, the fit looks very good and confirms that Weibull can accurately describe tsunami data.

The Weibull Plot is very useful; but, statisticians usually create a Probability Density Function (PDF) as shown below from Weibull Plot information. Such PDF graphs represent percent of population as area. (PDFs are fully explained later and also in Appendix C.)

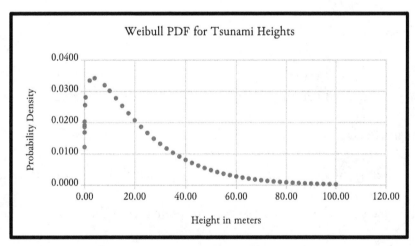

Figure 1-4: Weibull Tsunami PDF

PDF graphs are effectively histograms similar to Figure 1-2, but adapted to the continuous x number line in contrast to histograms which divide the x axis into various "range buckets". Because PDF Figure 1-4 is effectively a histogram, its shape should be similar to Figure 1-2. The reader should compare the two figures and confirm the following:

- Histogram 1-2 begins at x=0 and extends to x=100. Likewise for PDF Figure 1-4.

- The Histogram bar with "range bucket 0 to 20" is twice as tall as the following "range bucket 20 to 40." Likewise for PDF Figure 1-4.

- The 3rd ,4th & 5th histogram "range buckets" drop almost to zero height. Likewise for the PDF.

- For the histogram, left of x=0 falls to "nothing" and the PDF similarly collapses to 0 at the origin.

While minor differences are evident between histogram and Weibull PDF, both the x range and general shape are very similar. We next examine a Gaussian (or Bell Curve) analysis performed on the same data, create its PDF and make comparisons. It will be shown that the Gaussian (or Bell Curve) PDF grossly misrepresents the histogram.

Example Gaussian (or Bell Curve) Analysis:

When a data-set is analyzed by a Gaussian Distribution, a 3 step process forces the data to "give up" a mean and a variance which fully define the Bell curve PDF Figure 1-5.

- Document the data-set. (See Chapter 5 Problem 7 for tsunami data.)

- Take the average of the data-points (the average is called the mean in statistics).

- Find the average of the squared distances of points from the mean (i.e. the variance).

By using values of mean and variance computed above, an exact Gaussian Equation is written which (hopefully) describes the data. Spreadsheet use of the Gaussian equation creates PDF Figure 1-5.

Steps 2 and 3 of the Gaussian Analysis were performed by spreadsheet resulting in: mean μ = 22.34 and variance σ^2 = 530.84. Taking the square root the more commonly used standard deviation σ=23.04 is computed. For Gaussian analysis, there is no Weibull Plot equivalent, and hence no forcing of equation through data-points. The following Gaussian PDF is graphed based on mean and standard deviation .

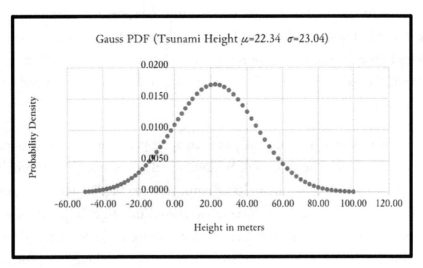

Figure 1-5: Gaussian PDF

As previously discussed, PDF graph (Figure 1-5) is really a histogram adapted to a continuous x number line. As such, the shape of the PDF should strongly resemble histogram Figure 1-2, BUT IT DOES NOT! Please compare Figures 1-2 and 1-5:

- Histogram Figure 1-2 begins at x=zero and extends to x=100. The Gaussian PDF begins at -50 and extends to 100. The Gaussian shows wrong data range.

- Histogram "range bucket 0 to 20" is twice as tall as the following "range bucket". PDF Figure 5 wrongly represents buckets "0-20 and 20-40" as equal in height.

- While the Histogram y value collapses to zero left of the origin, the Gaussian PDF has values beyond x=-40.

In general, the shape of the Gaussian Histogram is "just plain wrong."

13

Conclusions: Weibull vs. Gaussian

A Weibull description of Tsunami data does a reasonable job of describing the trends we see in the data but a Gaussian description does not. While the Gaussian description computes a true average height, it incorrectly indicates 20% of Tsunamis have negative height (i.e., are depressions rather than humps in the ocean). The Gaussian PDF also incorrectly indicates a wave of just over 20 meters is the most prevalent; but, Figure 1-2 shows that small waves are the most prevalent. Stated bluntly, the Gaussian "Bell Curve" misrepresents the actual distribution of wave heights.

For describing tsunami waves, Weibull analysis is an appropriate method of characterization and Gaussian analysis is not. The success of Weibull for this and many other problems results from the Weibull Plot which is unique in its attempt to force the Weibull equation through the data-points. A successful attempt at forcing equation through data-points is evidenced by tightly fit data-points about the straight Weibull line (Figure 1-3). Problems do exist where even Weibull cannot describe the data; but, in such cases, the Weibull Plot provides clear evidence of its inability. By contrast, a failed Gaussian analysis provides no clear signal of its failure; thus encouraging the analyst to assume "all is well."

Other Strengths of Weibull Analysis:

When Weibull is compared to other statistical distributions (Gaussian, Log Normal , etc.), Weibull exhibits a greater ability to twist and turn in conformance to data points. As a result, Weibull has greater likelihood of successfully describing a data-set. Figure 1-6 below illustrates the various shapes Weibull can take. Changes in the Eta (η) parameter, can stretch the shape horizontally if needed

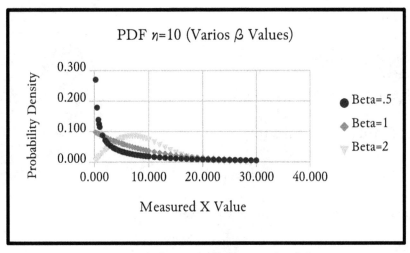

Figure 1-6: Weibull Shape Flexibility

It is possible to create a data-set that exactly represents a Gauss Distribution, or a Log Normal distribution or a decreasing Exponential Distribution. When tested against such data-sets, Weibull has been proven capable of describing all three.

When Gaussian analysis is used to analyze a data-set of 25 or more points, it is common to create a histogram to make sure that the Gauss PDF is similar in shape to actual data. Unfortunately, when small data-sets (e.g. 9 data-points) are analyzed, a convincing histogram cannot be made and other methods (e.g. Filliben's Probability Plot Coefficient Test for Normality) are needed. By contrast, the Weibull Plot provides clear evidence of either success or failure.

Finally, Weibull Analysis has been proven to successfully describe a wide range of phenomena. A few of the populations that have been characterized by a Weibull distribution include:

- Height of tsunami waves (5)

- Japanese earthquake severity (5)

- Size of fly ash in industrial smokestacks (4)

- Yield strength of Bofors Steel (4)

- Fatigue strength of St. 37 Steel (4)

- Fiber Strength of Indian Cotton (4)

- Stature of British adult males (4)

- Annual yield/acre for agricultural crops (5)

- Time interval between major earthquakes (5)

Chapter Footnotes:

1. The Great 1928 Japanese Tsunami is fiction. Illustration 1-1 is an Affinity Photo construct combining Hokosai's famous woodblock print with a model ship photo.

2. Data extracted from Wikipedia article on Tsunamis.

3. Historical data for tsunami heights is provided in Chapter 5 Homework, Problem 7.

4. A Statistical Distribution Function of Wide Applicability by Waloddi Weibull, ASME Transactions September 1951

5. The Weibull Bible by Paul F. Watson demonstrates successful Weibull analysis for a variety of phenomena.

Chapter 2: The Problems Weibull Can Address:

Using Weibull Analysis:

Weibull Analysis can address a wide range of statistical problems. In particular, Weibull Analysis can characterize a family of objects (the size of feet, strength of bolts etc.). Following

characterization, useful predictions can be made.

During World War I, America was called to send soldiers to Europe. Before making millions of army boots, the army needed a mathematical model describing the number of each size. The boot problem is typical of what Weibull Analysis can address.

Figure 2-1 Garr Williams (Public Domain)

Other Examples of how Weibull can be used follow:

- Based on the geologic history of Oregon, what is the likelihood of a major "off shore" earthquake in the next 10 years?

- Based on a test of 25 foundation bolts rated at 35 thousand psi, what percentage of manufactured bolts will have less than rated strength?

- Based on a survey of 20 Tillamook County dairy cows, what percentage of cows produce between 5 and 6 gallons of milk per day?

Weibull Analysis and the Probability Density Function (PDF):

The examples above require Weibull Analysis to correlate real world observations to likelihood of occurrence. <u>A PDF always describes the percentage of the population corresponding to different values </u>(e.g., What percentage of sharks are less than 6 feet long). In the language of statistics, Weibull Analysis uses data to identify a Probability Density Function (PDF) describing the underlying population. Note: The PDF is explained later in this chapter, in Appendix C and also at www.dionysus.biz St. Paul's Statistics.

Origin and Types of Real World Data:

A data set is created by observing results from a process consisting of a sequence of events. Events are either deterministic or stochastic. Deterministic events are totally repeatable given the same initial conditions, whereas stochastic events have random result (e.g. a coin flip has random result.) Repeatability is thus the "great divide" between deterministic and stochastic events. The terms Stochastic and Deterministic usually describe processes; but, for convenience, they will also be applied to corresponding data-sets (e.g. stochastic data-set)

Deterministic Processes: For a deterministic process, the observed "x" value is the consequence of the previous "x" value. The flight of a cannon ball for example, is a chain of predictable events, each determined by its predecessor's speed and direction. Deterministic data-sets are best analyzed by physics or other controlling laws and not by Weibull methods.

Stochastic Processes: For a stochastic process, an observed "x" data-point cannot be determined from prior values because the fundamental event is random. If a coin is "flipped" 26 times, the result of any "flip" is not contingent on the previous "flip" nor any "constellation of previous flips." Rather surprisingly, such random events do create patterns that can be analyzed statistically. Weibull and other statistical methods were developed to identify these patterns.

Mixed Process: For mixed processes, the "x variable of interest" takes a value based on an ensemble of deterministic and stochastic events. A data-set for such phenomena is likely to exhibit broad trends that are locally disturbed by random noise. For example, as summer turns to winter, climate cools; despite occasional and random temperature spikes. Statistical methods have been adapted to address a variety of mixed process data-sets.

Population Descriptive Data from Stochastic Processes:

Stochastic data is a sequence of measured values that represents some greater population of objects/people or events. When sorted, it is suitable for Weibull Analysis. An example follows:

Order Number	Salmon Length	Continued	Salmon Length
1	7.93	5	29.07
2	11.68	6	23.34
3	14.58	7	28.20
4	17.27		

Table 2-1: Salmon Samples

Population data consists of values for an observed property, at a "snapshot in time". The key idea is that the underlying population of objects has "preordained" and unchanging values. For the WWI boot example, if five men in a row had small feet, no doctor would have concluded "Today, men's feet are shrinking." The doctor assumes the constellation of foot sizes is fixed despite random observations. Population descriptive data is the ideal subject for Weibull or other statistical evaluation.

Limitations of Weibull Analysis:

- Weibull Analysis should be avoided when data is clearly deterministic.

- Weibull Equations may not fit a particular set of population data.

- Two parameter Weibull Analyses cannot model non-zero starting data.

- Small data-sets often cause substantial errors in statistical characterization.

Distinguishing Data-sets: Deterministic or Random?

Distinguishing between deterministic and stochastic data-sets is a complex subject. The paragraphs below provide examples followed by practical recommendations. For some data-sets, the data creation process is clearly deterministic and Weibull methods are not recommended. Cannon ball flight is one example. Global atmospheric warming is also deterministic, despite many complicating details.

Optional: Atmospheric warming is deterministic, based on a simple energy equation which balances incoming solar radiation with outgoing re-radiation. Net energy gain is converted to global warming. Complicating details include atmospheric CO_2 and dust concentrations, surface reflectance and cloud cover yet the process is deterministic.

For other data-sets, data creation is clearly random. Such random processes include "coin flipping," collisions between gas molecules and quantum mechanical interactions. For data-sets arising from these and similar processes, Weibull or other statistical methods are appropriate.

For many phenomena, a clear classification of deterministic vs. stochastic is elusive. Any of the following make classification difficult:

- Physics or other controlling laws may be poorly understood.

- The phenomena may be so complex that process mechanisms are not clear.

- The fundamental event mechanism may be difficult to observe (e.g. microscopic observables)

When classification is difficult, an examination of graphed data is often helpful. We usually expect weather related measurements to be random, but within defined bounds. Data from Kochi Japan over a 25 year period seems otherwise. Figure 2-2 shows annual Kochi wind speed exhibiting an almost linear 30% drop from 1950 to 1975. While random variation is evident, it seems unlikely chance alone is responsible for this protracted decline. Data behavior suggests the presence of some dominant deterministic mechanism that is reducing wind speed.

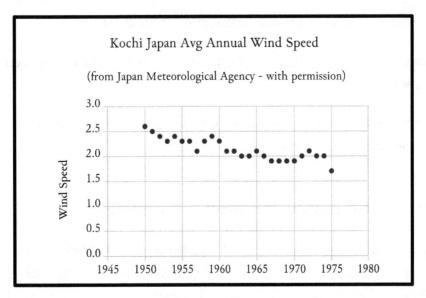

Figure 2-2: Kochi Wind Speed Trends

Data-set Evaluation (Deterministic vs. Stochastic):

A data-set can sometimes be shown to be stochastic based on probability first principles. For a group (salvo) of cannon shells fired together, the following statements are generally true:

- P is known: The probability of hitting the target is known from training exercises.

- Binary outcome: The result of each single shell is binary (it either hits or misses)

- Independent: The success of each shell is unaffected by success of the others in the salvo. (This is likely the most questionable of the 3 assumptions.)

The three conditions above are sufficient to declare the salvo impact pattern is stochastic. This seems odd, given that the flight path of the projectile is deterministic.

In most situations, a convincing argument based on first principles cannot be made and a stochastic determination follows a failure to demonstrate otherwise.

- Evaluation of known principles of physics or math as the fundamental event mechanism.

- Trial x-y spreadsheet graphing similar to Figure 2-2 to identify trending correlated to some other variable (such as year).

The Graphing Method for Data-set Evaluation

The graphing method asserts that a functional relationship observed between a variable of interest and some other variable is evidence of a deterministic relationship. Despite mathematical and philosophical concerns, use of the graphing method is often helpful.

Optional: While intellectually appealing and practical in application, there are problems with the underlying logic.

1. An ad hoc relationship between two variables does not identify the dependent vs. independent variable. If the variable associated with "our variable of interest" is simply "going along for the ride," it does not undermine a stochastic presumption for the variable of interest.

2. An ad hoc relationship between two variables may originate from relationships common to a third variable. e.g. An ideal gas exhibits relationships between pressure and temperature, but both of these quantities are related to a common third property (i.e. molecular velocity.) The evident functional relationships do not undermine statistical analysis of velocity.

Despite philosophical concerns, a spreadsheet search for ad hoc functional relationships will be discussed because it is easily accomplished and it often provides a path forward when other avenues have been exhausted.

A practical method to evaluate dependency of "variable of interest" on other variables is to use a spreadsheet to graph the data. From the graph, trends can be visually identified. The process of using a spreadsheet follows:

1. Create 2 columns for the data. Column B contains values for the "variable of interest." Column A contains corresponding values of a suspected causal variable.

2. Sort the two columns using Column A as the sort Index.

3. Plot the two column data using an x-y graphing option. Display trend-line and R^2.

4. Look at the plot. Does it obviously sweep up and to the right? Does it sweep down and to the right? Either suggests a functional relationship (and likely deterministic events). If it looks like a horizontally spread "shotgun blast," the stochastic hypothesis is supported.

5. Repeat for all variables that seem potentially causal.

Below are two examples of the graphing approach.

Example 1: Evaluating Kochi Japan Annual Rainfall for Trends.

1965	2425	1993	3355
1966	3422	1994	1835
1967	2353	1995	1909
1968	2470	1996	1733
1969	2206	1997	2153
1970	2590	1998	4383
1971	2039	1999	3581
...		...	
1986	1970	2014	3659
1987	2244	2015	2967
1988	2583	2016	2823
1989	3369	2017	2022
1990	3204	2018	3093
1991	2441	2019	2593
1992	2788		

Table 2-2: Kochi Rain Trends (3)

The data (with a few rows left out) is already sorted to evaluate time dependency.

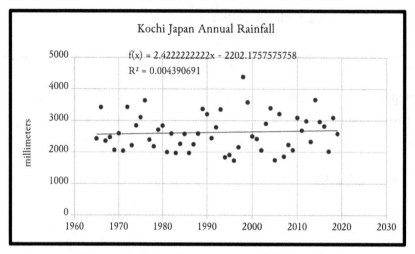

Figure 2-3: Kochi Japan Rainfall Trend

Figure 2-3 reveals a slight upward tilt of the "trend-line" from left to right. Total upward "climb" compared to scatter is small. Data thus appears to be a stochastic/random.

Example 2: Evaluating Cost of Early 20th Century Military Cannon. Based on cost of trucks and automobiles, there is a weak relationship between size and cost despite a Jaguar costing more than a flat-bed truck. Is this is true of military cannon?

The following data is from the US Army Journal of Artillery and shows the cost of cannon. This example strives to determine whether the cost of cannon is stochastic, or whether some kind of deterministic relationship is tied to size, weight or year. The data follows:

Year	Size (inch)	Weight (tons)	Cost	Source
1900	6	8.6	$42000	5
1904	6	8.6	$41000	5
1916	6	8.6	$48000	5
1916	8	14	$80000	5
1905	9.2	28	$58300	5
1900	10	29	$85250	5
1900	12	53	$90000	5
1916	12	53	$109000	5
1916	14	63	$114000	5

Table 2-3: Cannon Trends (4)

A quick review of Table 2-3 above indicates much greater cost impact associated with both size and weight rather than calendar year. Our evaluation thus focuses on Gun Weight and Gun Bore size. Figures 2-4 and 2-5 were prepared by spreadsheet in accordance with recommendations above.

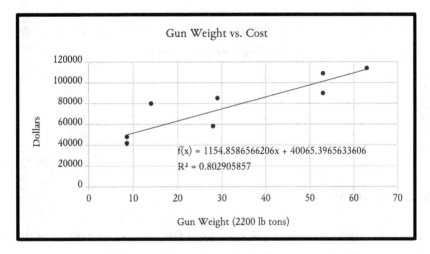

Figure 2-4: Cannon Weight & Cost

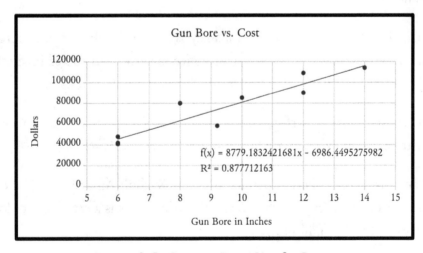

Figure 2-5: Cannon Bore Size & Cost

Data-point correspondence to a straight line in either figure above suggests a deterministic relationship affecting cost. The second figure has a steeper incline (slope of 8779 vs. 1154) and tighter data-fit (i.e. R^2 coefficient closer to the ideal value of 100%). Gun bore size is thus the dominant influence and the data is likely deterministic. Weibull or other statistical analysis should not be applied to this data, because deterministic methods are expected to make much better predictions.

Depending on the importance of a predictive model, a multi-variable analysis could be performed; but, is beyond the intended scope of this introductory text.

Chapter 2 Summary:

- Care should be taken to review a data-set to verify it is stochastic (not deterministic). Graphing the data is recommended as a "common sense" method for making a determination.

- If the data is deterministic, a statistical analysis such as Weibull is not appropriate and should not be attempted. In such circumstance, deterministic based predictions will likely be far more accurate than statistically based methods.

- Weibull Analysis can be performed with just a few data points; but, Appendix J demonstrates small data sets are likely to produce erratic results.

- Based on a stream of collected population data, Weibull Analysis provides clear methods for determining whether Weibull mathematics is a credible tool for analyzing the data (i.e. The Weibull Plot).

- If Weibull appears credible, clear Weibull procedures have been established that give direction for describing the underlying population (i.e.determining β and η). The Weibull Plot is the primary tool.

Chapter Footnotes:

1. Statement from Pier Paolo Ippolito, towardsdatascience.com, 8 August 2009

2. Kochi Japan wind speed data obtained from the Website of the Japan Meteorological Agency (jma.go.jp). See Appendix N for use authorization.

3. Kochi Japan annual rainfall data was obtained from the Website of the Japan Meteorological Agency (jma.go.jp). See Appendix N for use authorization.

4. Cost of Cannon: Most of the cost data is public domain, obtained from Journal of the United States Artillery, 1892 through 1903. Additional data is from Seacoast Fortifications of the United States Appendix B, by Emanuel Raymond Lewis, Copyright 1970 by Emanuel Raymond Lewis.

5. Oshima Wind Data: was obtained from the Website of the Japan Meteorological Agency (jma.go.jp). See Appendix N for use authorization.

6. San Juan Puerto Rico Rainfall Data from NOAA.gov for the years 2010 through 2019. See appendix N for use authorization.

7. The map of Japan associated with homework problems is a WWII period map and is in the Public Domain.

8. WWI illustration was created by American Cartoonist Garr Williams and is in the Public Domain. Extremely fine British artistic works were passed over due to the complexity of British Copyright law and it is hoped that the British government will take steps to clarify copyright claims with regard to this important historical period.

Homework Chapter 2:

1. Imagine and describe three examples of population data in ¼ page or less.

2. Imagine and describe an example of population data where time is the characterized variable in ¼ page or less.

3. Imagine and describe an example of deterministic data where Weibull Analysis should not be used. Document in ¼ page or less.

4. Based on information from the Japan Meteorological Agency (jma.go.jp) and graphed below, explain why you think Oshima wind data is Stochastic (random population type) or whether it is Deterministic (Strongly influenced by year). Note: Our thanks are to the Japan Meteorological Agency (5).

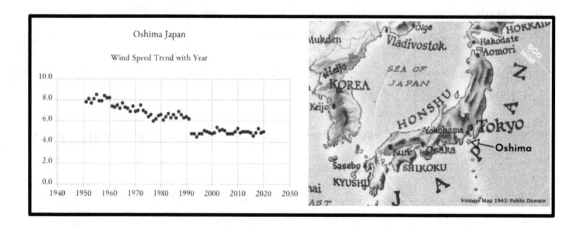

5.From NOAA.gov San Juan Puerto Rico data below for years shown (6), use a spreadsheet.

- Sort rainfall data in order by year & plot it with an x-y graph plotting option.

- Add linear trend-line & display trend-line equation.

- Based on visual appearance, state why you believe this is deterministic vs. stochastic data. Turn in graph and discussion to instructor.

	2010	2011	2012
Rain inches	85.3	88.6	68.3
	2013	2014	2015
Rain inches	71.1	58.5	74.2

Rainfall for San Juan Puerto Rico from NOAA

Chapter 3: Population, Data & Linear Conjecture:

Chapter 3 is a long journey through data-sets finally ending with the Linear Conjecture needed for computing Median Percents. It is easy to understand collection of data from a population; but statistical concepts are a "mash" of confusing ideas, so a whimsical explanation is offered.

A Scientist Collects Data:

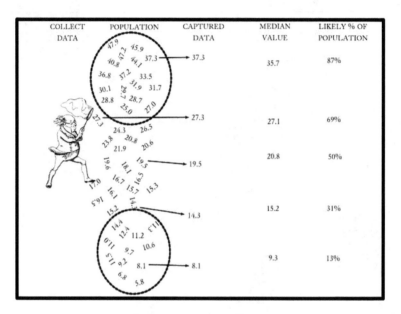

Figure 3-1: Scientist Collects Data

Figure 3-1 shows a scientist collecting data. The scientist swings his net to collect 5 samples. When samples are captured, they are typically spread out, representing small, medium and large members of the population. For five samples, there exist values that are the more likely to occur and they are shown in the 4th column. These are the Median Values corresponding to samples. Sample values also correspond to most likely population percentages (see 5th column) which are called Median Percents. In the ideal world, 5 samples from the population would match the 5 Median Values and would represent exactly the population percentages indicated by Median Percents. In reality, that's not what happens!

In the real world, the scientist swings his net capturing a number from somewhere in the population. Scientists are a clumsy lot, and thus have no control over the sample chosen. He simply swings and collects "somebody" from the population. When the scientist has all five samples, he arranges them in order from small to large.

The largest sample will likely be collected from the top elliptical region of Figure 3-1. The number might be any value within the ellipse (I assumed the largest value captured was 37.3 as shown in column 3). Because the ellipse is large and extends well into numbers "owned" by the data-point below, samples are often poor representations of their Median Values (i.e. the ideally expected values).

Due to chance, the smallest sample is likely from the lower elliptical region. Once again, probabilities dictate that the ellipse is quite "sloppy," overlapping the territory of its neighboring data-point. The sample data point is often a poor representation of its ideal population value (known as the 1st Median Value).

Data points 2, 3 and 4 all suffer the same malady of population misrepresentation. The data-set is thus a "sloppy" representation of the population, and Weibull Analysis must overcome these obstacles to produce a "best possible description" of the population.

Median vs. Mean:

In statistics, there are two extremely useful descriptions of central tendency of data-sets.

- The mean is the arithmetic average of all the data-points.

- The median is the dividing point value, below which half of all data-points reside.

We are more familiar with the mean; but, the median has proven far more useful for Weibull Analysis.

Differentiating Behavior of Median Value and Median Percent:

For a data-set of N values, there will be a population Median Value corresponding to each data-point i (1st through Nth). If a data-set is extracted from the population a very large number of times, the 2nd data-point Median Value can be found by:

- Sort all data-sets from small to large. (Note: "first" refers to the smallest value.)

- Take the collection of "2nd data-points". Find the value from among them exceeded by exactly half of 2nd data points. That will be the population Median Value for 2nd data-points. Of course this can also be done for the collection of 3rd data-points etc.

- We are interested in the Median Value for the population, rather than a small sample. Above, we stipulated a "very large number of samples" to ensure population Median Values are approximated.

By contrast, the Median Percent is the cumulative percent of population correlated to a Median Value. Curiously, while different populations have totally different Median Values, the Median Percents for the same size data-set are always the same. For example, for a data-set of five points, the 2nd data-point always corresponds to 31% of the population. This unique series of population percents depends only on size of the data-set and the position (1st ,2nd, ... last) of the data-point in question. (Note: the 1st is always the smallest data-point value.)

Median Percent Conclusions:

The following statements about Median Percent are true for all stochastic populations.

- A data-set of N values will have N Median Percents each corresponding to a data point number (i= 1st, 2nd ... N). These population percent values correspond to "most probable" percent of a population represented by each of the data-points.

- Median Percents depend only on ordered position of data point (i=1,2,3 ...) and the size of the data-set (N). We can thus compute Median Percent for the 3rd data-point (i=3) for a data-set of 23 data-points (N=23). Details of the population or data-points make absolutely no difference.

The Median Percent for point i of N total data points can be estimated by Benard's Equation or computed exactly from the Linear Conjecture based equation:

Benard's Equation:

$$Median\% \sim \frac{(i + .3)}{(N + .4)}$$

The Linear Conjecture:

$$m = \left[2 \cdot .5^{\left(\frac{1}{N}\right)} - 1\right] \cdot \left[\frac{1}{(N-1)}\right]$$

$$b = .5^{\left(\frac{1}{N}\right)} - \left[\frac{(2 \cdot N)}{(N-1)}\right] \cdot \left[.5^{\left(\frac{1}{N}\right)} - .5\right]$$

$$MedianPercent = m \cdot i + b$$

For above equations:

- i = data point (1st, 2nd, ... Nth) who's Median Percent is desired

- N = number of data points in the data set

The remainder of this chapter will examine how data-sets evolve, the basis for believing in Median Percents and the Linear Conjecture which unites this body of information. It also provides useful equations needed for Weibull Analysis. Probability Density Function graphs will be used in the pages that follow. At any time, the reader can get a review of the PDF, from either Appendix C, or from http://www.dionysus.biz/StatisticsIntroduction.html

Naive Concept of Median Percent:

The first steps for performing a Weibull Data Analysis are:

- Collect data and sort it from smallest to largest value.

- Establish Median Percents corresponding to each data-point.

For five light-bulbs allowed to "burn until failure", failure times might be as follows:

Fail Order	Time to Failure	Median Percent
1	3.72 weeks	12.9%
2	6.09 weeks	31.5%
3	8.33 weeks	50.0%
4	10.82 weeks	68.5%
5	14.28 weeks	87.1%

Table 3-1: Time to Failure

Many readers will rebel, insisting that 1st, 2nd ... 5th failures correspond to 20%, 40%, 60%, 80% and 100% of failures; however, the preceding discussion emphasized that Median Percent refers to percent of population (not of sample). While 14.28 weeks is the best sample, a huge data-set almost certainly contains better light-bulbs, thus 14.28 weeks cannot represent 100% of population. The following pages should clarify this distinction between "percent of test sample" and "percent of parent population."

Data Concepts and Data Presentation:

It is easy to trivialize the relationship of an ordered data-set to its population; yet, there are subtle aspects that are important. This chapter will show that a stream of ordered data representing a population has meaning, even if "stripped" of numerical values. Sequence alone enables certain conclusions. Additional statistical ideas are discussed in the following paragraphs.

What is a Statistical Population?

From Schaum's Statistics by Murray R. Spiegel p1: "Population= The entire group of like objects that a study attempts to characterize." Examples of possible populations follow:

- The population of historical off-shore Oregon/Washington region earthquakes.

- The population of annual Texas cotton yields.

- The population of persons receiving COVID-19 vaccine.

What is a Data-set and Why Do People Collect Them?

Data-sets are generated either by testing, or by observing worldly phenomena. A data-set is a collection of observations enabling inference of either a deterministic law, else population trends. Statistics, involves the latter. For statistics, a data-set is thus the "fodder that feeds analysis" intended to reveal population likelihood of observing "this vs. that." For the light bulb example, the intent of collecting data should be to determine the percentage of light bulb population failing with ever increasing usage time. The intent is not to determine how the data-sample behaves .

Population Variation & Presentation:

All populations exhibit variation of some characteristic. Athletic coaches look for students who run the fastest. Agricultural agencies look for regions that produce the most with levels of production eagerly recorded. Frequency characterization is the act of associating observation value range to percent prevalence in the population. Two ways of depicting frequency distribution are:

- Population histogram based on percentage.

- Population Probability Density Function (or PDF).

Figures 3-2 and 3-3 describe the frequency distribution for annual Texas cotton yield based on USDA Data (2). It is vitally important to understand that the probability of an observed event falling within a range of x values, is the Area of the PDF graph between those same x values. This will be illustrated by the following figures.

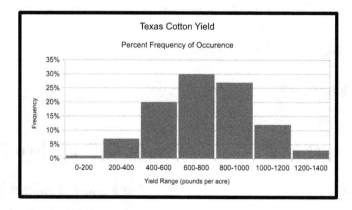

Figure 3-2: Texas Cotton Histogram

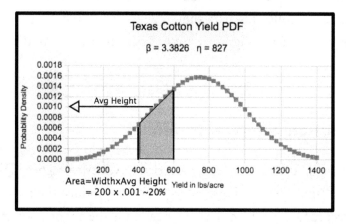

Figure 3-3: Texas Cotton PDF

The two figures convey the same information and have similar shape. The PDF works much better for Weibull Analysis than the more understandable histogram.

Comparison of Histogram to PDF:

The population histogram bars must total 100% because the histogram (Figure 3-2) represents the entirety of cotton yield (all of it). While the percent histogram shows yield percent corresponding to various bars (e.g. 20% of annual yields were between 400 and 600 lb/acre), a bit of arithmetic can extract this same answer from the PDF. Let's compare the 3rd bar of Figure 3-2 to the gray shaded area of PDF Figure 3-3. The PDF represents percentage as area under the curve. The PDF shows an "eyeball estimated" average height of the shaded area. At lower left of the figure, the shaded zone area is computed as 20%.

For the third bar, we have shown histogram and PDF area indicate the same percentage of years for the same yield range. The histogram only displays percentage frequencies for specific ranges, but PDF enables (awkward) computation of percentage for any desired range.

- The PDF displays percent between x=0 and x=a as area under the curve.

- There is also a Cumulative Density Function (CDF). It is an equation (or graph) that represents the same data but avoids area estimation. The CDF equation can be derived from the PDF equation. The CDF equation directly computes PDF area.

Importance of the PDF:

The PDF Equation corresponding to a set of data, is the fundamental description of the underlying population. It is thus the basis for all generalizations and alternative descriptions. The following can be generated from the PDF.

- PDF equation can be used to produce the visual PDF Graph (see Fig 3-3)

- The CDF equation can be derived by calculus integration of the PDF equation.

- The CDF equation enables direct computation of area corresponding to any x value.

- All predictions about a population are made on the basis of either the PDF or CDF.

Data-point "cluster" about "preferred x locations:"

Patterns Arise from Data-Sample Collections: Typical Experiments

An experiment is usually performed only once, and a single data-set results. The population under study is often quite large compared to the limited number of samples chosen. As a result, there is a huge number of possible data-sets, and chance determines whether the experimenter's data-set is truly representative, or whether it is some atypical outlier.

In the following sections, we examine the extent of data variation among the multitude of possible data-sets. We begin by examining the possible consequences of performing the same test three times, thus obtaining three data-sets with each "claiming" to represent the same population. Our goal is to gain insight into likely data variability whenever we collect data. That is, we want to know whether repeated experiments produce similar results.

Data-sets and their Behavior in the IDEAL WORLD:

Consider an experiment which obtains four length measurements from a shark population. Let's consider what may happen IN THE IDEAL WORLD if an experiment is performed three times, with data-sets ordered and plotted together. One IDEAL WORLD possibility is quite unexpected as illustrated below.

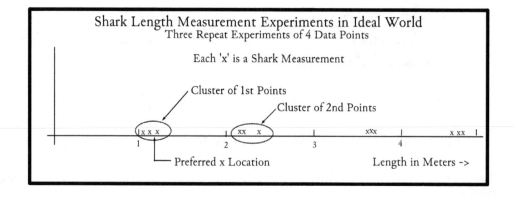

Figure 3-4: Ideal World Data-set Clumping

38

We instinctively expect the data-points to be scattered in a quasi-uniform fashion along the x axis; but, let's consider another possibility. Based on Figure 3-4 above, the population of sharks is spread from about one to six meters in length. Shouldn't we expect the smallest of four randomly picked sharks to always be about the same length and near to 1 meter? Out of four sharks, shouldn't we expect the largest sample to be about 5.5 meters (out of 6 meter maximum)? Isn't it credible that data will "cluster" into groups corresponding to the 1st, 2nd, ... and 4th data points?

This ideal world interpretation of a "three times" experiment is shown in Figure 3-4 above. It shows four distinct clusters of data-points, with the first cluster representing "the trio of first data-points." In the "Cluster of 1st Data-points", we see three distinct x values, each representing a 1st shark length data-point.

The same pattern is repeated for the cluster of 2nd data-points suggesting that "Population" gives up data-samples clumped around "preferred x locations." In the sections that follow, we will investigate the truth or falsity of two hypotheses:

- Data points from repeated experiments "cluster" into visually distinct groups of observations, with each group corresponding to ordered data point number (1st, 2nd,

- There is a central tendency (center x location or Median Value) for each data cluster. The series of Medians form an ordered progression of steps

In the sections that follow, examples based on both real world and computer synthesized Weibull data-sets will be used to investigate hypotheses 1 and 2 above. It will be shown that hypothesis 1 is false. It will be shown that hypothesis 2 is credible.

Data-sets in the REAL WORLD:

If we examine results of repeat sampling of real world data-sets, data overlap between clusters is typical and "white space" between data clusters vanishes.

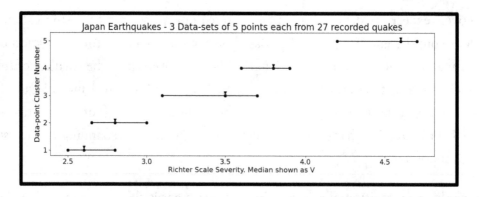

Figure 3-5: Three Times Experiment. Japan Earthquakes

Figure 3-5 above is based on 27 instances of Japanese earthquakes all within a single month. (3) The "x" recorded variable is earthquake Richter scale severity. To simulate repeated experiments, three different data-sets (consisting of five data-points each) were randomly extracted from the population of 27 actual earthquake occurrences. Each of three data-sets was ordered by sorting.

In Figure 3-5, the three "first data-points" were plotted together and joined by a horizontal bar, thus representing the first data-point "cluster". The three "second points" were treated likewise etc., until all five data clusters were represented by the figure.

Figure 3-5 shows overlap between the 1st cluster and 2nd cluster and likewise between the 3rd and 4th clusters. Elsewhere, clusters are distinct (i.e. do not overlap their neighbors); but, absence of clear boundary zones between domains of the 2nd and 3rd makes visual distinction impossible.

We summarize our observations about Figure 3-5 as follows.

- Hypothesis 1: (observably distinct data clusters) is apparently false.

- Hypothesis 2: (progressive and ordered "midpoint" tendency) appears possible.

Data-sets in the REAL WORLD Using Synthetic Data:

The statistical distribution of a real world population is usually not obvious. Synthetic (computer generated) Weibull data-sets can be created with known β and η. When studying data behavior, these are advantageous because the exact population characteristics giving rise to data-points is known. The graphs that follow are based on such synthetic test data extracted from a Weibull population of 200 data-points.

Figure 3-6 was created based on a synthetic five point data-set, extracted for each of 3 experiments. The "three times" experimental results were graphed in Figure 3-6 below and are comparable to the repeated Japanese earthquake data sets at the left. In addition to plotting the "data clusters" the Median Value of each "cluster" is identified. Note: Synthetic data-sets do not represent Richter Scale values.

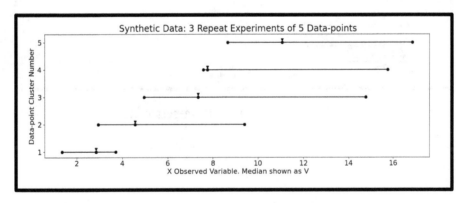

Figure 3-6: Synthetic Data - 3 Data-sets of 5 Points

Figure 3-6 invites conclusions consistent with the Japanese earthquake data.

- Hypothesis 1: (observably distinct data clusters) Once again seems false.

- Hypothesis 2: (progressive and ordered "midpoint" tendency) Appears credible.

To form a definite opinion about propositions 1 and 2, we must examine more examples. In particular, we should examine the results as the total number of data-points is increased. This can be done in either of two ways: By increasing the number of data points in each of our three experiments or by holding the data-point count at five, but increasing the number of repeat experiments. We will first examine a three times repeated experiment, each of 12 data-points.

Figure 3-7 shows graphic evidence of data cluster domains for 1st, 2nd, ... 12th data-points. Central tendency measure (median) is again plotted as basis for evaluating the 2nd proposition.

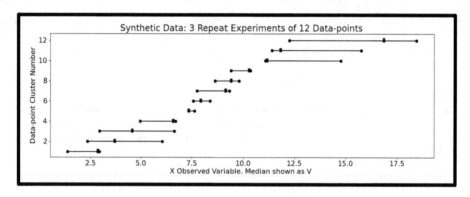

Figure 3-7: Synthetic Data - 3 Data-sets of 12 Points

Increasing data-point count in each test makes visual distinction of data-clusters impossible as an overlapping "muddle" results; but, data center bar positions are ordered and progressive. Conclusions for Hypotheses 1 and 2 follow:

- Hypothesis 1: (observably distinct data clusters) Is clearly false.

- Hypothesis 2: (progressive and ordered "midpoint" tendency) Increasingly credible.

The remaining method of increasing total data-point count, is to increase the number of repeat experiments (from 3 to 36) while maintaining a data-point count of five. Once again, computer generated data-sets based on the same Weibull population were used.

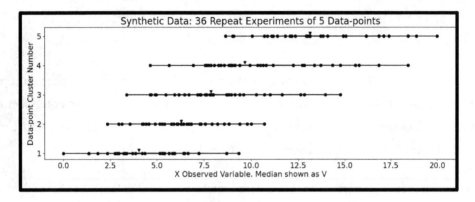

Figure 3-8: Synthetic Data - 36 Data-sets of 5 Points

Examination of Figure 3-8, confirms earlier surmise that increased total number of data-points (by whatever means) results in utterly indistinguishable data clusters. Comparison of Figure 3-7 (36 total data-points) to Figure 3-8 (180 total data-points) indicates that larger total data-point count better defines central tendency for data-clusters.

- Hypothesis 1: (observably distinct data clusters) Is clearly false.

- Hypothesis 2: (progressive and ordered "midpoint" tendency) Appears true. A progressive and fairly uniform "stair step" increase of median value is evident.

The notion of observably distinct data clusters has been disproven but the clumping of all first data-points around a central position seems confirmed (likewise for 2nd data points etc.). The central "preferred x positions" and the associated percentage of population have special importance for Weibull Analysis as discussed in the next section.

Median Percent, Concept and Estimation:

Deeper Investigation of Median Value:

The preceding graphs from repeated data extractions demonstrate that data points (1st through last) cluster around central values. By definition, central point x locations of data clusters are the Median Values for data-points. Note: In statistics, Median indicates an equal number of values above as below.

From Figure 3-8, it may also be observed that the data-point concentration near data point Medians is dense, and thins towards the left and right extremes of data-clusters. A central concentration of data points combined with thinning at the ends suggests each "cluster" is really a distribution of points around some central value as illustrated below.

When an experimenter measures data, each of his measurements is from the "cloud of possible data-points" which is a random x value selected from the corresponding PDF "cloud".

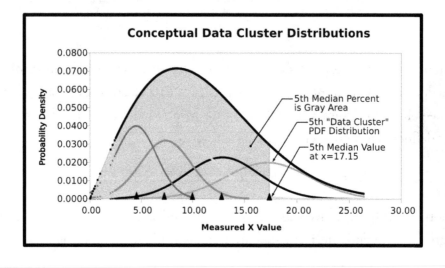

Figure 3-9: "Data Clouds" about Median Value

Optional: "Data Clouds" for 1st through Nth data-points are not Gaussian as shown, but the illustration correctly associates the "data cloud" to the Median Value and the correlated Median Percent. 5th Median Percent is aligned with Median Value as shown.

Concept of Median Percent (as distinct from Median Value):

One of the first steps in Weibull data analysis is to compute Median Percents represented by each of the data-points. <u>The Median Percent of the 5th data-point is the cumulative percentage of population corresponding to the 5th Median Value</u>. It is thus the gray shaded area of Figure 3-9. Similar Median Percents are defined for data-points 1 though 4. It is crucial to understand that this "5th Median Percent" identifies population percentile for the 5th point distribution mid-point. Thus the Median Percent is 50% likely to exceed a randomly selected 5th data-point (also 50% likely to be less).

Diagrams similar to Figure 3-9 can be drawn representing distributions with various PDF shapes. Interestingly, when the PDF shape changes, data-point Median Values shift to accommodate; but, Median Percents remain unchanged. It is thus apparent that Median Percents are very fundamental realities of data-sets, and Median Values "go along for the ride."

Estimating Median Percents from Experimental Data:

Median Percents can be determined in two ways. They can be based on repeat experiment data-sets, or on probability theory. We will examine the experimental method first.

The figure below repeats the familiar 36 repetition data-set collection, each of 5 data-points; but a shaded box has been drawn surrounding experimental data-points less than the Median Value of first data-points. A Python routine was written to count the number of data-points less than the Median Value indicated on the figure (originally I did it with a magnifying glass). If the count of points is divided by the total number of data-points (180), the answer should approximate the Median Percent of population for the 1st data-point.

For the first Median Percent estimation, 22 points divided by 180 total points indicates 12.2% of the population is below the Median Value ("data cluster center"). This closely approximates the mathematically accepted value which is 12.94% (See Appendix A for confirmation.)

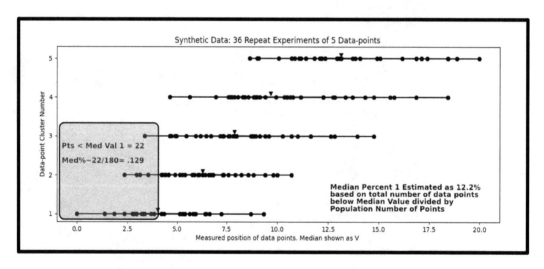

Figure 3-10: Experimental Estimation of Median Percent

The same process can be performed to experimentally estimate the Median Percent corresponding to the 2nd of five data-points as shown in figure 3-11 to the right.

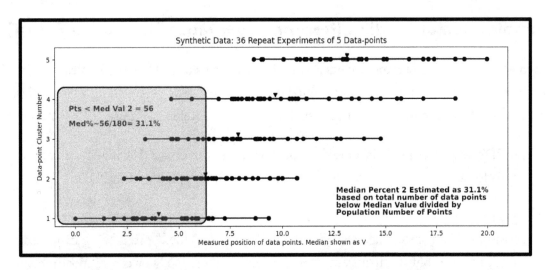

Figure 3-11: Experimental Estimation of Median Percent

Based on Figure 3-11, the percent of total population falling below 2nd Median Value can be determined. This is Median Percent. By counting, 56 data-points out of 180 fall below the 2nd point Median Value. Dividing determines a 2nd Median Percent as 31%. The same method was followed for 3rd, 4th and 5th points and results are presented in Table 3-2 below which also compares experimentally determined values to math theory based values.

Data Point	Test Median%	Math Median%
1	12.2%	12.9%
2	31.1%	31.5%
3	51.7%	50.0%
4	71.7%	68.5%
5	88.9%	87.1%

Table 3-2: Experimental vs.Theory Based Median Percents

We have already seen that data-points from repeated experiments are "peppered" around their Median Value, with some greater and some less than central tendency. As a result, a data-point rarely represents its "proper percentage of population." While an actual data point may not represent a theory based value, Median Percent still corresponds to that "most likely" position. Thus concepts of "Median Percentage of population" and "most likely x position" are related.

Determination of Median Percents from Math Theory (1st & last)

Mathematicians avoid data-experiments as a basis for conclusions. They prefer clear assumptions and logical steps that determine precise answers. For determining first and last Median Percents, the following are the basis for argument. (Refer to Figure 3-12 as needed)

- A PDF representing ANY closed shape having interior area = 100% will be used as the basis for argument. Conclusions from the proof thus apply to ALL PDFs.

- Median Percent is cumulative percent of population, for most likely data-point x position. We acknowledge data-points are "full of mischief," often being displaced from ideal location; but Median Percent is defined by "most likely or central position".

- Because Median Percents correlate to data-point Median Value (central x location), it is 50% likely a randomly chosen point will fall to right of its Median Percent.

- The area under a PDF between points x=a and x=b, is the probability that a randomly chosen member of the population will fall between those two values.

- If the probability of event is p%, then the probability of two repetitions is p%^2. The probability of N repetitions p%^N.

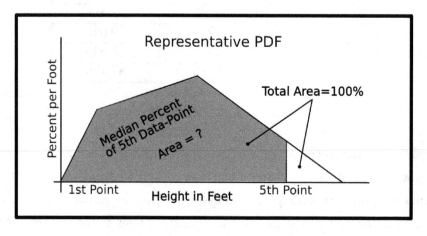

Figure 3-12: Last Median% by Theory

The PDF for a population describes the percentage likelihood of finding a data-sample within a specified range of x values. If an experimenter selects and sorts five items for a data-set, their x values will occupy various positions on the PDF x axis. Because they are sorted, no sample x value can exceed that of the 5th point.

By definition, 5th Median Percent is the percent shaded area of Figure 3-12 which is 50% likely to contain the 5th, and all previous points.

- The probability of the 1st (smallest) data-point being in the gray area is p%

- The probability of the 2nd data-point being in the gray region is p%

- The probability of the 3rd ....

- The probability of the 4th ....

- The probability of the 5th data-point being in the gray region is p%

The probability of all five being so located is p%^5 which must equal 50% for a median.

p%^5 = .50 Taking the 5th root of both sides results in: p%=.5^(1/5) => .5 ^.2 = 87.05%

Writing the equation for the more general case of N data-points (in lieu of 5):

Eq 3-1: $$LastMedian = .5^{\left(\frac{1}{N}\right)}$$

Equation 3-1 is a general expression for computing the Median Percent for the last of N data points. Comparison of 87.05% (for five data points) with published tables shows this result to be correct (see Appendix A for a table of accepted values.)

49

Determining the 1st Median Percent for 5 Data-Points:

Determination of the 1st Median Percent can be similarly accomplished.

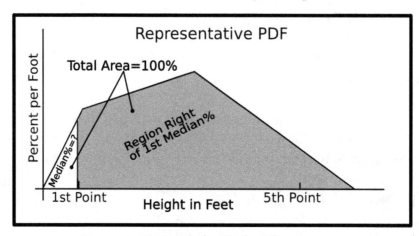

Figure 3-13: 1st Median% by Theory

The representative PDF illustration is revised as shown above.

- The Median Percent corresponding to the white region is 100%-Grey%

- The Grey % requires that p%^N=50% => p% = .50^(1/N)

- White area = 1 - .50^(1/N) which is the Median Percent for the 1st of N data-points

$$\text{Eq 3-2} \qquad \boxed{1stMedian = 1 - .5^{\left(\frac{1}{N}\right)}}$$

For a 5 point data-set, a pocket calculator confirms the first median as 12.94% consistent with published values for the 1st Median Percent of 5 data-points. Questions follow:

- What is the fifth Median Percent for a data-set of 5 points? Answer: 87.06%

- For 5 data-points, is it always 87.06% regardless of the kind of distribution? Yes.

- For 17 data-points, is it 87.06%? No. Apply Eq 3-1 using N=17.

Why Data-points "Clump" Around Median Values:

Data-point "clumping" is the result of probability peaks at certain x locations. The sections that follow explain this phenomena and will identify methods to compute Median Percents corresponding to any desired data-point.

The Newly Discovered Linear Conjecture:

Traditionally, the 1st through Nth Median Percents are computed using the rather confusing Binomial Theorem (see Appendix D) or by the approximate Benard Equation. This book presents the newly discovered Linear Conjecture method, discovered by the author and believed presented herein for the first time. The Linear Conjecture method offers the following advantages:

- A clear conceptual framework for understanding Median Percents.

- A tolerably simple closed form equation which computes exact Median Percents.

Determining 1st Through Nth Median Percents by Linear Conjecture Equation:

The Linear Conjecture Equation: where N=data-set size (number of points) and i = data-point number

Eq 3-3

$$m = \left[2 \cdot .5^{\left(\frac{1}{N}\right)} - 1\right] \cdot \left[\frac{1}{(N-1)}\right]$$

$$b = .5^{\left(\frac{1}{N}\right)} - \left[\frac{(2 \cdot N)}{(N-1)}\right] \cdot \left[.5^{\left(\frac{1}{N}\right)} - .5\right]$$

$$MedianPercent = m \cdot i + b$$

Example: Find the 4th Median Percent for a data-set of 7 points. (i=4, N=7). Usually, the analyst must compute Median Percents for all N data-points. Computing m and b separately facilitates their repeated use by simply "plugging in" successive data-point numbers in the equation m*i+b. This greatly speeds the calculation process during problem solution.

Eq 3-4

$$m = \left[2 \cdot .5^{\left(\frac{1}{7}\right)} - 1\right] \cdot \left[\frac{1}{(7-1)}\right] = .13524$$

$$b = .5^{\left(\frac{1}{7}\right)} - \left[\frac{(2 \cdot 7)}{(7-1)}\right] \cdot \left[.5^{\left(\frac{1}{7}\right)} - .5\right] = -.040965$$

$$MedianPercent(4) = 0.13524 \cdot 4 - .040965 = .49995$$

Discovery of the Linear Conjecture:

I first discovered linearity of median percents after graphing point number vs. median percent for five data-points. My graphing used published values of Median Percent. I was shocked by the obvious conclusion that interior points are linearly spaced with data-point number. I next graphed examples with various numbers of data-points, always reaching the same conclusion. The table and graph below illustrate my discovery using a data-set of 7 points.

Seven Data-Point Example of Linearity of Interior Median Percents.

1st Point	2nd Point	3rd Point	4th Point	5th Point	6th Point	7th Point
9.4%	22.8%	36.4%	50.0%	63.5%	77.1%	90.5%

Table 3-3: Median Percents for 7 Data-points (5)

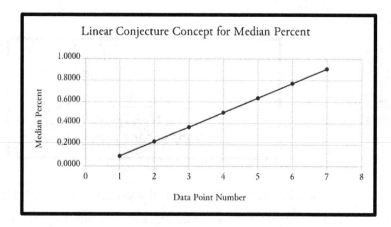

Figure 3-14: Median Percent Linearity

After many examples confirmed the linear hypothesis, a brute force confirmation of the Linear Conjecture was developed and became the technical basis for Equation 3-3 above.

Optional: Basis for the Linear Conjecture and its Equations:

Median Percents corresponding to a set of N data-points are needed to identify a Weibull Equation corresponding to a data-set. The Linear Conjecture provides clear concept and closed form equations; but a mathematical proof of the Linear Conjecture is problematic. Appendix E provides "brute force" justification. Appendix E presents a Python 3 program used to compute Median Percents by the Linear Conjecture that are then tested for accuracy by substitution into the Binomial Equation (method explained in Appendix D) for all Median Percents belonging to data-sets from 3 points to 1000 points. By definition, a correct Median Percent must compute 50% probability of occurrence .

Data-set Range	Target	Max Err	Run Time
3-20	50	8.88e-16	5.94 sec
3-50	.50	4.66e-15	35.92 sec
3-100	.50	1.144e-14	132.40 sec
3-250	.50	3.059e-14	3927.58 sec
3-1000	.50	1.213e-13	56560.91 sec

Table 3-3: Linear Conjecture Validity Test

If Median Percent determinations were exact, the maximum error column would contain zeros indicating the .50 Median Target value was precisely achieved. While .50 was missed, actual check sums are miniscule, the difference resulting from computer round-off errors. In the author's estimation and supported by published tables, Median Percents computed by the Linear Conjecture are accurate to 4 or more decimal places. See Appendix D for a summary of the Binomial Equation methodology, and Appendix E for details of the Python Program used to confirm The Linear Conjecture.

Linear Conjecture Conclusions about Data-sets:

The 1st and last point's Median Percents are determined by Equations 3-2 and 3-1. These equations do not apply to points 2, 3, 4 ... N-1. The population PDF is thus divided into 2 external regions (external to 1st & last points), and an internal region where contributions of the Linear Conjecture are paramount. The following three graphs illustrate what the Linear Conjecture says about data-sets and Median Percents.

General Conclusions from the Linear Conjecture:

The following figures convey step by step conclusions that arise from the Linear Conjecture. The figures assume five point data-sets, but the principles apply to data-sets of any size.

Figure 3-15 emphasizes that the 1st and last Median Percents for a data-set of five points can be computed by previously determined equations. The implications concerning the central area are rather obvious.

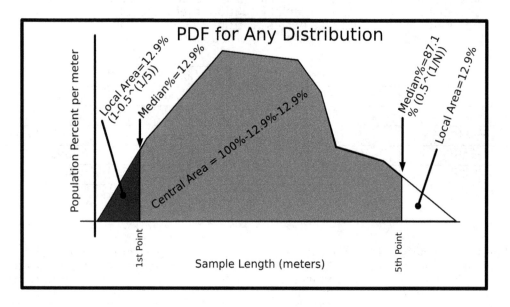

Figure 3-15: 1st & Last Median% Determined by Equation

From Figure 3-15 above, the percent area of the central area is easily computed. But the Linear Conjecture requires equal areas for the 4 (i.e. N-1) regions representing the 2nd, 3rd, 4th and 5th Median Percents. Why? The sequence 1, 2, 3, 4, 5 has increments of one. A linear relationship requires the corresponding y increases to be uniform to produce a constant slope between between all the points.

This results in Figure 3-16 which computes the common local area, based on four equal divisions of the known internal area (74.2% divided by 4 = 18.5%).

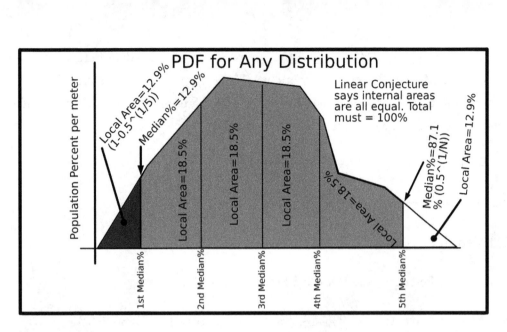

Figure 3-16: Linear Conjecture Requires Equal Partition of Central Region

Finally, the Median Percents are progressive. i.e. each is the previous Median Percent increased by the additional area "picked up" as we move through the local area.

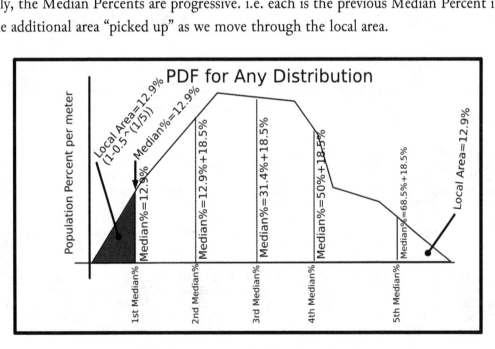

Figure 3-17: Progressive Median Percents Computed

As illustrated in Figure 3-17, Median Percents are progressive. A Median Percent ALWAYS equals the previous Median Percent + Increment. The Linear Conjecture states that all (central region) increments are the same (about 18.5% for 5 point data-sets). The sequence of Median Percents can thus be computed as shown below:

- 1st Median Percent: 12.9%

- 2nd Median Percent: 12.9%+18.5% = 31.4%

- 3rd Median Percent: 12.9%+18.5%+18.5% = 49.9%

- 4th Median Percent: 12.9%+18.5%+18.5%+18.5%=68.4%

- 5th Median Percent: 12.9%+18.5%+18.5%+18.5%+18.5%=86.9%

Note: Values above are computed to 3 place accuracy.

Median Percents + PDF Shape Determine Median Values:

Optional: A Median Value is the most likely position for a test data point (e.g. most likely x value for the 1st data point). The position of a Median Value may be determined by its Median Percent and the PDF shape of the population using "key steps" provided below. In steps below, we assume the number of data-points is five (N=5).
- The Median Percent of the 1st data-point can be calculated from Equation 3-2.

- The 1st Median Value is found by "sliding" Fig 3-18 right boundary line (labeled Median=12.9%) to the right or left, until the trapped area really is 12.9%. Simply put the boundary somewhere, estimate width and height of the trapped region and compute the area. If area is wrong, adjust boundary position and recompute until the correct position for Median Value is found.

- The trapped area between Median Percents 1 and 2 is computed as shown by Figure 3-16. For five data-points, interior trapezoidal regions ~ 18.5%.

- To determine the 2nd Median Value, slide the right boundary (labeled Median=31.5%) somewhere left or right and estimate the newly formed trapezoidal area. If the newly formed area is not equal to 18.5% computed above, adjust the right boundary position and recompute. Continue to adjust and calculate until the trapezoidal area is correct indicating Median Value is found.

- Repeat the last step until all Median Values have been determined.

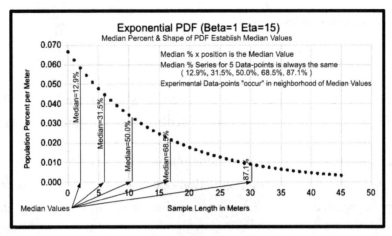

Figure 3-18: Finding Median Value

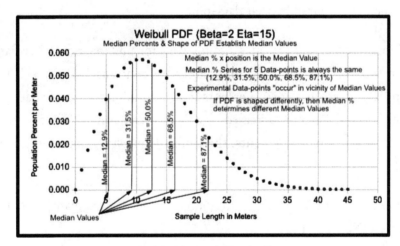

Figure 3-19: Typical Weibull PDF

Two PDFs are shown above. The method described works on both, but the Median Values determined will differ because the PDF shapes are different.

We may conclude that Median percents are very fundamental aspects of data-sets. When used along with PDF shape of the population, Median Values can be determined; however, there are easier ways.

If the Weibull Plot indicates a population is truly Weibull, then one of the equations provided in Appendix H will allow computation of all the Median Values.

Chapter 3 Conclusions:

<u>Data-sets:</u>

- Data sets are collected to characterize the underlying population (not the data-set). Data-points should be correlated with Median Percents (not percent of test sample.)

- Repeat experiments involving the same phenomena may produce very different descriptions of the underlying population due to random data-point drift. This problem is severe for small data-sets (i.e. 20 data-points minimum is recommended).

<u>Linear Conjecture:</u>

- The Median Percent for a data-point is the cumulative percent of population most likely to be represented by that data-point.

- The Linear Conjecture provides a framework for understanding Median Percent. 1st and last Median Percents are computed from Equations 3-1 and 3-2. For data-sets of known size, all other Median Percents (corresponding to integer data points) are the previous Median Percent increased by a fixed increment. While this enables computation of Median Percents, the Linear Conjecture equation is a better method.

- The Linear Conjecture provides the basis for derivation of an exact closed form equation (Eq 3-3) that precisely computes any desired Median Percent for a data-set of known size N.

- Justification for the Linear Conjecture is provided (Appendix E) based on brute force demonstration of accuracy for data-sets ranging from 3 to 1000 data-points. Beyond 1000 data-points, Median Percent approaches percent of population.

- The Linear Conjecture equations for Median Percent are accurate beyond 4 places.

Chapter Footnotes:

1. See Schaum's Statistics by Murray R. Spiegal Page 1, McGraw-Hill Book Company, copyright 1961.

2. Texas Cotton Yield was obtained from the U.S. Department of Agriculture website.

3. See Appendix N for use authorization. Japanese earthquake data was obtained from the Japan Meteorological Agency (jma.go.jp) web site.

4. See Appendix N for use authorization.

Homework Chapter 3:

1. In your own words, describe how percent probability is described on a PDF graph. You may use a hand drawn figure if you like. Please do not use more than 1/2 page.

2. If there are only 5 "wormworts" in the world, and they are named: Athena, Ben, Casey, Dan and Elaine:

   - How many possible data-sets of 4 samples exist?

   - Show each possible data-set (list all items of each data-set by name).

   - Use no more than 1/2 page.

3. For a data-set composed of 7 data-points:

   - Compute the 1st Median Percent using Equation 3-2.

   - Compute the last Median Percent using Equation 3-1.

   - How many median percents are there?

   - Show all work.

4. For a data-set composed of 6 data-points:

   - Compute the 1st Median Percent using Equation 3-2.

   - Compute the 1st Median Percent using Equation 3-3

   - Did you get the same answer? Show all work.

5. For a data-set of 5 points. Complete the table shown using any method.:

Ordinal Number	Median Percent
1	
2	
3	
4	

6. Using the completed table from problem 5 above, and using either graph paper or computer spreadsheet, make a precise graph using "x axis" for the Ordinal Number and "y axis" for Median Percent. If the graph is made using a spreadsheet, use the "create x-y" graph option for the correct kind of graph.

Describe what the graph looks like in about 3 sentences.

Turn in completed Table, Graph and description to your Instructor.

7. In your own words, describe the Linear Conjecture. You may use hand drawn graphs if needed. Please do not exceed 1/2 page of text (if you use graphs, you may use however many you like.)

Chapter 4: Routine Median Percent Computation

Determination of Median Percents can be accomplished by any of four methods:

1. The Linear Conjecture based Equation 3-3.

2. The approximate Benard Equation

3. Binomial Equation based trial and error computer solution. (Explained in Appendix D)

4. Tables of Median Percent (See Appendix A).

The two practical methods for calculating Median Percent are the precise Linear Conjecture based Equation, and the approximate Benard equation. Because the Linear Conjecture is newly discovered, analysts are unaware of it, and most routinely use the approximate Benard Equation. The Linear Conjecture based equation for Median Percent is thoroughly justified and its development explained in Appendix E

Linear Conjecture Based Equation and Computation:

The Linear Conjecture equation is accurate and practical for scientific calculator, spreadsheet or computer program. The method works for data-sets of any size and can compute the Median Percent corresponding to any data-point number. The equation may be used with fractional data point ordinal numbers such as the 3.25th data-point as discussed below.

During performance of engineering or scientific life duration experiments, a few data samples are sometimes prematurely removed due to laboratory equipment issues. When such testing demonstrates survival of samples to certain times, but not to intended failure, they are called discarded (or suspended) data-points. As shown in later chapters, when data-samples are prematurely discarded, Weibull Analysis applies methods to adjust the ordinal positions (1, 2, 3 ...N) usually resulting in fractional ordinal positions (e.g. 1, 2.25, 3.25 ...). The Linear Conjecture based equation is accurate with fractional as well as integer ordinal numbers.

The Linear Conjecture Equation: where N=number of data-points & i = data-point number

Eq 4-1

$$m = \left[2 \cdot .5^{\left(\frac{1}{N}\right)} - 1\right] \cdot \left[\frac{1}{(N-1)}\right]$$

$$b = .5^{\left(\frac{1}{N}\right)} - \left[\frac{(2 \cdot N)}{(N-1)}\right] \cdot \left[.5^{\left(\frac{1}{N}\right)} - .5\right]$$

$$MedianPercent = m \cdot i + b$$

It is obvious, that expressions for m and b above can be substituted into the Median Percent equation immediately above resulting in a single, closed form equation:

Eq 4-2

$$MedPrct = \left[2 \cdot .5^{\left(\frac{1}{N}\right)} - 1\right] \cdot \left[\frac{1}{(N-1)}\right] \cdot i + .5^{\left(\frac{1}{N}\right)} - \left[\frac{(2 \cdot N)}{(N-1)}\right] \cdot \left[.5^{\left(\frac{1}{N}\right)} - .5\right]$$

Where: N = total number of data-points in data-set   and i = data point number (1, 2, ...

While Equation 4-2 is satisfying, practical analysis relies on Eq 4-1

Benard's Equation - An Approximation for Median Percent:

Benard's Equation is a simple and reasonably accurate method for estimating Median Percent. It works for a data-set of N samples, and computes Median Percents for i = 1st data point, i=2nd, ... i=Nth data point. It also works for fractional Ordinal Numbers. Example:

Eq 4-3 Benard Eq: Median Percent = (i-.3)/(N+.4)   For a data-set of 5 points, N=5

- For the 1st data-point: -> Median Percent = (1-.3)/(5+.4) = 12.96%

- For the 3rd data-point: ->Median Percent = (3-.3)/(5+.4) = 50.00%

- For the 3.25th point: ->Median Percent = (3.25-.3)/(5+.4) = 54.62%

Typical errors of the Benard Equation can be assessed by comparing Benard Equation results to published Median Percents shown in Table 4-1 below and are usually less than 1%.

Data Point	Median	Benard Eq.	Error
1	12.94%	12.96%	.18%
2	31.38%	31.48%	.32%
3	50.00%	50.00%	0.00%
4	68.62%	68.52%	.15%
5	87.06%	87.04%	-.03%

Table 4-1: Accuracy of Benard's Equation

The Benard Approximation is usefully accurate, and can be trustingly applied to most problems. It is only in situations requiring great conservatism that something better may be required. While Linear Conjecture based Equations are a strong competitor to the Benard Equation, the latter is very simple and its accuracy usually sufficient.

Binomial Equation Based Median Percent Computation:

The Binomial Theorem can be used to generate probability equations. These equations can describe Median Percents for Weibull populations. Unfortunately, the resulting equations cannot be algebraically solved for more than four data-points. Higher order equations require trial and error solutions implemented by computer methods.

A second issue is that each data-set size results in a different equation; thus the computer based trial and error solution must be run for each different size of data-set.

A third issue is the method only works for integer ordinal numbers. This means that whenever a data-set includes discards (suspended items), Median Percents cannot be directly computed by the binomial method. A data-point with adjusted ordinal of 2.25 thus requires linear interpolation based on ordinals 2 and 3. While interpolation is not difficult, the fractional ordinal issue adds yet another inconvenience.

A technical explanation of the Binomial Equation approach to Median Percents is provided in

Appendix D. Prior to discovery of the Linear Conjecture, the Binomial approach was the only precise means for determining Median Percents. Much like "Z Tables" associated with the Gaussian Distribution, the Binomial Equation was historically used to create tables enabling practical use of the results.

Tables of Median Percent:

Given that Median Percents (based on the Binomial Theorem) are tedious to compute, computer generated tables of Median Percent have been published. (e.g. Appendix A). Published tables provide Median Percent values for integer data-point ordinal number with separate columns for different sized data-sets. While difficult to find, these tables address various sizes of data-set. Because most data analysis problems require the Weibull analyst to obtain Median Percents for each of N data-points, tables can be convenient.

	3 points	4 points	5 points	6 points
1st	20.63%	15.91%	12.94%	10.91%
2nd	50.00%	38.57%	31.38%	26.44%
3rd	79.37%	61.43%	50.00%	42.14%
4th		84.09%	68.62%	57.86%
5th			87.06%	73.56%
6th				89.09%

Table 4-2: Table of Median Percents

Table 4-2 indicates that for five samples, the Median Percent for the last data point is 87.06% which is in agreement with previous calculations. Table 4-2 also provides values for the first through fourth data-points which are less easily computed.

If an analysis requires Median Percent for a fractional data-point location (called a fractional Ordinal Value or in The New Weibull Handbook it is called an adjusted rank) such as 2.25 for five data-points, linear interpolation of Table 4-2 can be used. Two alternative analytic methods (Linear Conjecture and Benard's Equation) enable computation of fractional Ordinal Number Median Percents without linear interpolation. Within the overall scheme of Weibull Analysis, tables are an awkward means of advancing analysis. They can serve as a "fast lookup tool," and are important for verifying other methods.

Presentation of methods to compute Median Percent for a data-set of whatever size is now complete. But before ending this chapter, it is a convenient time to investigate how often data-points "lie".

Do Data-Points Often Lie?

The simple answer is "Yes". This means they very often are not close to their expected position or Median Value. The question of data-set "honesty" is perhaps best answered by determining the percentage of data-points that grossly misrepresent their Median Values for five point data-sets. Table 4-3 tabulates results based on Figures 3-5 to 3-8.

Data Point	Overruns Neighbor	50% Err Relative to Median Value
1	13.9% of data-points	44.4% of data-points
3	50% of data-points	13.9% of data-points
5	25% of data-points	2.8% of data-points

Table 4-3: Percent of Data-Points Misrepresenting Median Value

The table shows that any data-point (from a data-set of five) is about 25% likely to badly represent its Median Value either in terms of percent error, or in terms of over-running its near neighbor Median Value. Single data-points cannot be trusted.

In general, statistics works well with large data sets, and erratically with small data-sets. For a large data-set, it is rather unlikely that most or all of the data-points will fall above their expected values (recall probability of p and p = p^2). Other disruptive behavior such as false linear decrease trending is similarly unlikely. It is thus a well founded conclusion that larger data-sets are far more dependable predictors of population than smaller data-sets. While there is no absolute number that is "good enough", I recommend 20 points minimum, and analysts should simply refuse to work with less than 5 data-points.

I am at odds with authors who believe "A strength of Weibull is its ability to analyze small data-sets." I caution that small data-sets are treacherous.

Returning to A Simple Question:

We began Chapter 3 by asking why five data points representing "burn-out" time of light bulbs do not have Median Percents 20%, 40%, 60%, 80% and 100% . We now know the answer. The sequence above represents test item percentages, but does not fairly represent percentages of the underlying population. From Table 4-2 we know that five data-points weakly corresponds to 12.94%, 31.38%, 50.00%, 68.62% and 87.06% of the population.

Chapter Summary:

For a data-set, each data point (i.e. 1st, 2nd etc.) is most likely to represent a certain cumulative percent of the population the data-set was selected from. For five data points, the 1st is most likely to occupy the x position corresponding to 12.94% of the population. The 2nd to 31.38%. The Median Percent sequence (12.94%, 31.38% ...) is a list of these percent values for five point data-sets. The Median Percent list differs for each data-set size.

When confronted with a data-set, Median Percents for each ordered data-point "i" can be computed by either of 2 practical methods:

- The exact Linear Conjecture based equation (for any data-set size)

- The very simple Benard approximation (for any data-set size)

Chapter Footnotes:

1. Median Percent tabular values extracted from The New Weibull Handbook, Appendix I, written and published by Dr. Robert B. Abernethy, Copyright 1993.

2. Queensland Shark Catch Data is available from the Queensland Government web site, and is distributed with a Public Commons license. See Appendix N for terms of usage.

3. Fort Monroe Gunnery Practice Data: Public Domain Data: Journal of the United States Artillery, Vol. 4 No. 4 1895

Homework Chapter 4:

1. Find Median Percents for each of 8 data-points by using the Appendix A Table of Median Percents. Data has already been sorted. (2)

2017	Shark Species	Length (m)	Median Percent
1	Blacktip	.20	
2	Blacktip	.76	
3	Blacktip	.90	
4	Blacktip	.94	
5	Blacktip	.95	
6	Blacktip	.98	
7	Blacktip	1.10	
8	Blacktip	1.20	

2. Using the data-set from problem 1, compute the Median Percents for each data-point by the Benard Equation. Compare the results with answers from problem #1.

3. An engineering experiment is planned that will stress cycle 36 bolts to failure. Benard's equation will be used to determine Median Percents.

- If the experiment is stopped after 20 bolt failures, what is the number of samples N used for calculation of Median Percents?

- If the experiment is stopped after 25 bolt failures, what is the number of samples N?

- If the experiment is continued until all 36 bolts fail, what is the number N?

4. An engineering life test of a mechanical drive design determined the number of revolutions prior to failure. The test stand provided simultaneous testing of six drives. Before end of the allocated test time, four failures occurred at the indicated revolutions. Student should reconstruction the table to include sorting.

A	B	C	D	E	F
Sample No	Fail Cycles	Sample No	Fail Order	Ln(Cycles)	Median%
1	4382			Blank	Blank
2	Discard 2800			Blank	Blank
3	1735			Blank	Blank
4	3770			Blank	Blank
5	Discard 948			Blank	Blank
6	801			Blank	Blank

5. During 1891 Fort Monroe practice, 51 eight inch cannon shells were fired at a target with "miss distance" shown below. Convert to ordered data-set & calculate Median Percents for the first 10 data-points by Benard's Equation (Use a spreadsheet if you like)

	Miss (yards)		Miss (yards)		Miss (yards)
1	300	18	10	35	300
2	350	19	200	36	40
3	100	20	50	37	90
4	25	21	250	38	200
5	30	22	5-	39	10
6	200	23	500	40	350
7	100	24	0	41	300
8	5	25	100	42	8
9	5	26	77	43	14
10	20	27	50	44	300
11	500	27	10	45	15
12	50	29	100	46	12
13	25	30	350	47	300
14	200	31	350	48	15
15	10	32	14	49	200
16	60	33	25	50	300
17	200	34	6	51	600

6. For the data set sizes listed below, compute First & Last Median Percents by any method.

Data Point Number	First	Last
4		
5		
6		
7		

7. The IQ of 6 Gorillas trained to communicate using American Sign Language is provided in the table below. Create an ordered data-set from the information given. Compute Median Percents for each subject.

	Name	Sex	IQ
1	Otto	M	78
2	Sally	F	80
3	Beth	F	93
4	Tom	M	95
5	Lola	F	85
6	Tam	F	97

Note: Information above is simulated data and does not represent any scientific study. For historical context, Koko the gorilla was raised by anthropologists and trained to speak ASL sign language. Koko learned to understand 2000 words of English and could respond with approximately 800 ASL sign language words. During her 47 year life, she received 3 intelligence tests with a median IQ score of 90. Her IQ testing was based on modified human IQ tests.

8. For a data set of 6 points, compute the Median Percent for the 1st, for the 2nd ... for the 6th data point using each of the following methods.

- Linear Conjecture based Equation

- Benard's Equation

Chapter 5: Characterizing Weibull Populations
(2 parameter analysis)

Chapter Goals:

Before Weibull predictions can be made, the population must be characterized from sample data. Data must be evaluated to determine which (if any) of the possible Weibulls describes the data. The purpose of this chapter is to show you how to determine the population shape parameter β and scale parameter η that fully describe a 2 parameter Weibull Distribution.

Approach for Identifying Population Parameters β and η:

When a population is discovered in the "wild" (perhaps a German bearing factory) the analyst has no basis for guessing the shape of its population PDF and it might be any of the shapes below else entirely different. While Weibull can model the first three, it cannot succeed with the 4th or many other shapes.

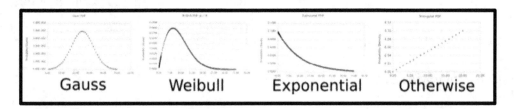

Figure 5-1: PDF Shapes that May Describe Data

The analyst has one further handicap. He/she has few samples and it has already been shown that data-points are often poor representations of population Median Values.

Figure 3-1 illustrated the data collection process based on all of the possible values within the population. Figure 5-2 on the following page shows the same population stripped of information not known by the analyst. Weibull Analysis provides effective methods for extracting useful population information from sparse information available.

Information Known to the Analyst:

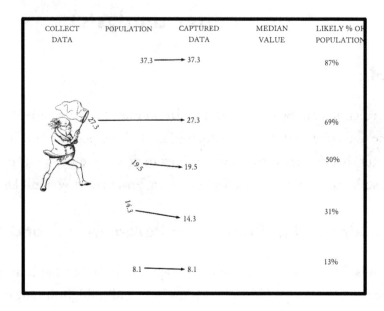

Figure 5-2: Information Actually Known to Scientist

If the data included five Median Values and five Median Percents, there is a method for:

- Converting Median Values to Pseudo X values

- Converting Median Percents to Pseudo Y values

When this is done, the pseudo values are plotted on x,y grid and slope of the line forced through data-points is the β parameter we need. Unfortunately, we do not know the Median Values. Instead, we have only a data-point from the cloud surrounding each Median Value. The heart of the Weibull Plot method is use of data-points as proxies for Median Values. Thus

- Convert data-point values to Pseudo X values

- Convert Median Percents to Pseudo Y values

A best possible straight line is forced through the pseudo X,Y points. The "fit line" should approximate the line resulting if actual Median Values were used (since a data-point is from the cloud of possible data-points around its Median Value). Because we are approximating Median Values, we should expect random data-point scatter about the "fit line". The resulting Weibull Plot should look similar to Figure 5-3 below:

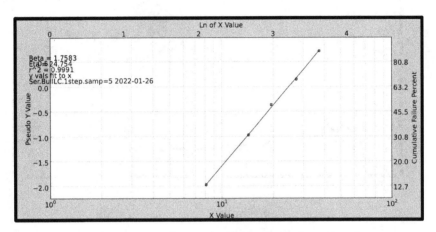

Figure 5-3: Example Weibull Plot Based on Proxies

Observations about Weibull Plot Figure 5-3:

- If the population really conforms to a Weibull equation, a straight line based on Median Values would pass exactly through data-points; but because proxy values were used in lieu of Median Values, data-scatter about the line is inevitable.

- Small scatter above and below the line is acceptable. Figure 5-3 is far better than can be expected for real world data; but, large scatter, sharp crooks, or curves formed by the data-points indicate problems with using Weibull to describe the population.

- The R^2 value is a measure of data-point scatter with 100% indicating a perfect fit. $R^2 < 90\%$ indicates Weibull conclusions should not be trusted. $R^2 > 93\%$ usually indicates reasonable Weibull representation of the population.

- Figure 5-3 shows a straight line slope of 1.7583 which is the β parameter value. A β value of 1.7583 indicates a PDF similar in shape to Figure 5-4 with $\beta = 1.8$

73

Weibull is a Family of PDF Shapes:

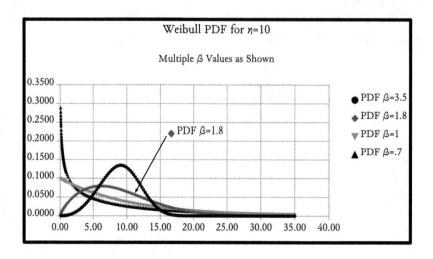

Figure 5-4: Weibull PDF Shape Flexibility

Example of Weibull Characterization of β and η for a Data-set:

In 1905 Europe, concrete was often made by mixing cement, stone dust from crushing mills, and gravel; but in America, engineers insisted on torpedo sand in lieu of rock dust. As a senior project in civil engineering, Mr. Whitney prepared samples (using sand vs. stone dust) and performed compression strength testing to determine which made stronger concrete. Mr. Whitney's results for sand prepared concrete follow(1):

Test Sample	Strength psi
1	808
2	1591
3	842
4	1638
5	1422
6	1015

Table 5-1: Concrete Strength Data

Example: Use a Watson Standard Template from Appendix B and a spreadsheet to:

1. Sort (small to large) and Document data-set.

2. Make a spreadsheet that generates x,y pseudo plot points.

3. Use the spreadsheet to create a Weibull Plot based on x,y pseudo plot points.

4. Determine β and η that correspond to the data. Determine R^2

5. Evaluate Weibull Plot and discuss whether Weibull seems appropriate for this data-set

Step 1: Document data. Use Watson Standard Template (or spreadsheet) as below.

- Complete "Order" & "Data Value" columns. Data should be ascending sorted.

- Ignore "Blank" columns

- "Rank" values are copied from "Order" column (because we have no discards)

- "Median" is computed by either Benard Equation (Eq 4-3) or Linear Conjecture (Eq 4-1) based on "Rank" values

Order	ContraOrd	Data Value	Discard	Rank	AdjRank	Median
1	Blank	808	Blank	1	Blank	10.94%
2	Blank	842	Blank	2	Blank	25.56%
3	Blank	1015	Blank	3	Blank	42.19%
4	Blank	1422	Blank	4	Blank	57.81%
5	Blank	1591	Blank	5	Blank	73.44%
6	Blank	1638	Blank	6	Blank	89.06%

Table 5-2: Watson Std. Template w/o Discards

Step 2: Make a spreadsheet that generates x,y pseudo values for plotting.

- Columns A, B and C are copied from Watson Standard Template.

- Spreadsheet functions are used to compute columns D and E as shown below.

A	B	C	D (pseudo x)	E (pseudo y)
Rank	Data	Median	Ln(Data)	LnLn(1/(1-Med%))
1	808	10.94%	=Ln(808)	LnLn(1/(1-.1094))
2	842	25.56%	=Ln(842)	Etc.
3	1015	42.19%	Etc.	Etc.
4	1422	57.81%		
5	1591	73.44%	Etc.	0.2819
6	1638	89.06%	7.4012	0.7943

Table 5-3: Spreadsheet Example- Graphing Pseudo x,y

Step 3: Use spreadsheet to create a Weibull Plot using values from Col D & E of Table 5-3.

- Highlight Spreadsheet Right 2 columns. Choose "graph", using X-Y (Scatter) option.

- Right-click any data-point. Choose "Add Trend-Line","Show Linear Eq. & R^2 "

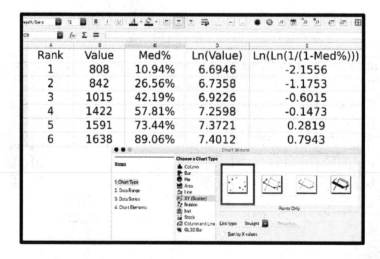

Figure 5-5: Weibull Spreadsheet & Plotting

And finally, the result is the Weibull Plot shown below.

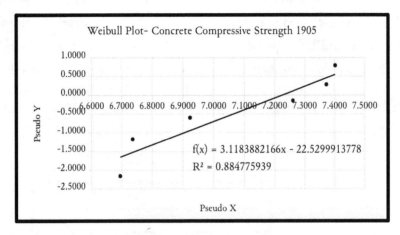

Figure 5-6: Weibull Plot of Concrete Compressive Strength

Step 4: Determine β and η:

- β=3.1184 Beta is the numerical value of slope from equation in Figure 5-6

- η = e^[-(-22.52999/3.1184)] = 1373.2 Note: Eta is computed by calculator

- Read R^2 directly from Figure 5-6 (provided you requested it plotted)

Step 5: Visually evaluate ... and discuss ...

"While Weibull data behavior is likely, R^2 values less than 90% are not recommended. As expected from the low R^2 value, data-points are somewhat 'ragged' about the fitted line. The lowest point seems to diverge unnaturally from the 'fit line.' "

If Weibull results are for a non-critical use, Figure 5-6 provides barely credible evidence that the population can be represented by a Weibull PDF and determined values of β and η might characterize the underlying population. Ragged data scatter about the fitted line and low R^2 value indicate that conclusions are untrustworthy and reports should include disclaimers.

Writing the Weibull PDF Equation:

Weibull Equations are discussed in Chapter 6; however doing a great deal of work to produce values, one for β and one for η seems unrewarding. To put this achievement into perspective we now derive the Weibull PDF Equation based on the 1905 concrete test data. We will also graph the equation to get visual confirmation that our equation looks reasonable.

The Weibull PDF Equation: The general form of the 2 parameter Weibull PDF follows:

Eq 5-1
$$WeibullPDF: f(x) = \frac{\left(\beta \cdot x^{(\beta-1)}\right)}{\eta^{\beta}} \cdot \frac{1}{e^{\left(\left(\frac{x}{\eta}\right)^{\beta}\right)}}$$

Substituting $\beta = 3.1184$ and $\eta = 1373.2$ results in the particular Weibull matching the data:

Eq 5-2
$$f(x) = \frac{\left(3.1184 \cdot x^{(3.1184-1)}\right)}{1373.2^{3.1181}} \cdot \frac{1}{e^{\left(\left(\frac{x}{1373.2}\right)^{3.1184}\right)}}$$

PDF Eq 5-2 is an ugly looking mess. While potentially useful, it is difficult to know if it is correct. One way to judge is to graph it and look at the result.

To graph Eq 5-2, I used a spreadsheet. Column A listed raw x values (not pseudo x) from .01 to about two times η (i.e. x in range .01 to ~2700) in steps of 100 to produce about 20 data-points. The y values were computed from Eq 5-2 based on the x column. Despite questionable looking spreadsheet numbers, the PDF plot below confirms our answer. PDF Figure 5-7 looks like a respectable Weibull PDF with a Beta value of about 3. Compare Figure 5-7 to Figure 5-4. (Note: Figure 5-4 had Eta=10 which "crunched" the high point of the curve to about that value but Figure 5-7 has Eta=1373 thus its peak resides slightly left of that value.

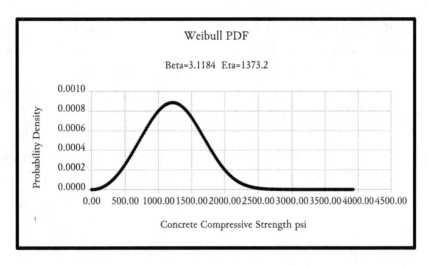

Figure 5-7: Optional: Weibull PDF from Eq 5-2

Suspended (or Discard) Data and the Watson Template:

Watson Standard Templates are worksheets that encourage a consistent approach to Weibull Analysis. Appendix B provides two versions of the Watson Standard Template. One is for data-sets without Discard Data, and the other is for data-sets with Discard data. The short explanation is that Discard Data (also called suspended data) is data that has some defect that prevents it from being treated statistically like all the other data. Examples of Discard Data are provided below, but please be aware it is not "totally thrown away" because it can contribute to the accuracy of β and η estimates.

During engineering life tests, it is common to simultaneously expose multiple like samples to a test environment. Often, each sample is instrumented. If for example, a response accelerometer "falls off" of a test sample and cannot be replaced, then the time of "falling off," its discard status and a brief explanatory note are recorded against that particular data point. It can't be called a failure and its survival is only proven for part of the test duration.

Weibull Analysis is conducted differently when "discarded data-points" are present. Appendix B consequently provides a template specifically for data-sets that include one or more discards.

The templates guide the "occasional" analyst through the correct analysis steps, and eliminate column computations (blanked out) not needed for current circumstance. Both Watson Standard Templates can be found in Appendix B and may be freely copied for use in reports, published materials, books, etc.. If published, please identify as "Watson Standard Template", or "Modified Watson Template" as appropriate.

Homework assignments are broken into two sections. Homework Section 1 provides problems that do not include Discard Data. Homework Section 2 includes problems that include Discard Data points.

Homework Chapter 5 Section 1:

Weibull Data Analysis without Discard Data

1. Kochi Japan Rainfall data was analyzed for the period 2010 through 2019 and the following two plots resulted. The first is a trend plot of year vs. rainfall to determine whether deterministic influences were present. The second is a Weibull Plot to determine if Weibull is appropriate for analysis, and to determine β and η. (Source: Japan Meteorological Agency. (2))

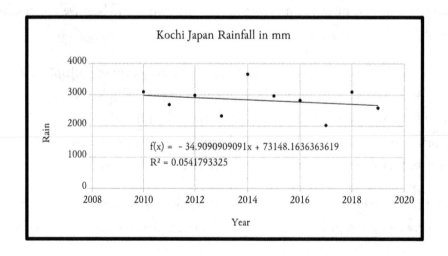

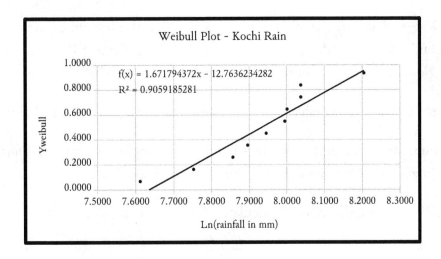

Weibull Plot - Kochi Rain

$f(x) = 1.671794372x - 12.7636234282$
$R^2 = 0.9059185281$

In a quarter page or less, document your thoughts on whether the "trend plot" suggests the data "does/does not" have a strong deterministic influence.

- Assume a Weibull Analysis should be pursued. Study the Weibull Plot. Does it indicate Weibull modeling is appropriate? Please justify your answer in a quarter page

- What do you suppose the very low R^2 value for the trend study means?

- Based on the Weibull Plot shown above, what is the β value?

2. The previous example problem for concrete strength provided data for concrete made with sand. The data below is from samples made with stone dust. (Public Domain Data (1))

Test Sample	Strength psi
1	1619
2	1672
3	1678
4	1731
5	1782
6	1857

See Steps a through g on next page:

Part a: Use Watson Standard Template for Data-set without discards (or equivalent). Fill out applicable columns based on table above. Use Benard's Median Percent Equation from Chapter 4 as needed. Note: the strength values in Template must be sorted before all else.

Part b: Complete a spreadsheet table similar to Table 5-3 to support a Weibull plot.

Part c: Use a spreadsheet to create a Weibull Plot using the right most two columns from step b. Include a "trend-line" type linear. Display linear equation and the R^2.

Part d: Compute η by using a scientific calculator. (note: $\eta = e^{\wedge}[-(b/m)]$ also β = the Weibull Plot slope)

Part e: Write 1/8 page describing whether the Weibull plot indicates Weibull is appropriate.

Part f: Print or copy the Watson Standard Template, Weibull Plot, β and η and turn in.

3. The Queensland government maintains a shark control program which monitors shark catches, documenting the species and length. Data for 2017 follows:

	Species	Length (m)		Species	Length (m)
1	Tawney	2.00	9	Tawney	2.60
2	Tawney	2.80	10	Tawney	2.10
3	Tawney	2.60	11	Tawney	2.10
4	Tawney	1.90	12	Tawney	1.90
5	Tawney	2.65	13	Tawney	2.30
6	Tawney	2.40	14	Tawney	2.26
7	Tawney	2.69	15	Tawney	2.76
8	Tawney	2.00			

Perform steps a) through f) from problem 2 above.

Queensland Government website. Use permission is documented in Appendix N.(12)

4. United States Center for Disease Control monitors seasonal Flu infections and publishes estimated total symptomatic infections by season. The data below documents ten flu seasons and corresponding symptomatic illness counts. (Source: CDC. (3))

Ordinal	Season	Infections
1	2010-2011	21 million
2	2011-2021	9.3 million
3	2012-2013	34 million
4	2013-2014	30 million
5	2014-2015	30 million
6	2015-2016	24 million
7	2016-2017	29 million
8	2017-2018	45 million
9	2018-2019	36 million
10	2019-2020	38 million

Perform steps a) through f) from problem 2 above.

5. The USDA monitors crop production rates in the United States. The following table documents cotton lint yield in pounds per acre for the indicated years. (source: USDA. (4))

	Year	lb/acre		Year	lb/acre
1	2000	730	11	2010	902
2	2001	1059	12	2011	1038
3	2002	1110	13	2012	928
4	2003	1056	14	2013	847
5	2004	890	15	2014	840
6	2005	870	16	2015	896
7	2006	720	17	2016	1056
8	2007	920	18	2017	960
9	2008	768	19	2018	933
10	2009	849	20	2019	916

Perform steps a) through f) from problem 2 above.

6. The Japan Meteorological Agency monitors earthquake occurrence in Japan. The following table documents 27 earthquakes during October 2020. Severity is by the Richter scale. (5)

Date	Place	Mag	Date	Place	Mag
11 Oct 20	Oki Miyagi	3.6	14 Oct 20	Fukushima	4.3
11 Oct 20	Hokubu...	2.2	15 Oct 20	Hyuga...	2.9
11 Oct 20	Tokara...	3.2	15 Oct 20	Okuubu...	3.8
11 Oct 20	Satsuma..	3.7	15 Oct 20	Tokara-ret..	3.5
11 Oct 20	Mayakejimi..	2.6	15 Oct 20	Chichijim..	4.2
11 Oct 20	Oki Miyagi	2.9	16 Oct 20	Tokara-ret..	2.5
11 Oct 20	Urakawa..	3.8	16 Oct 20	Engan-ho	3.7
12 Oct 20	Osaka-fu...	3.1	16 Oct 20	Amami-Oshi.	3.3
12 Oct 20	Oki Iwate	3.2	16 Oct 20	Hokubulba.	3.8
13 Oct 20	Noto-chiho..	2.8	17 Oct 20	Chuetsu-..	3.9
13 Oct 20	Nakadoni..	3.7	17 Oct 20	Nambu..	2.1
13 Oct 20	Hokutobu..	3.0	17 Oct 20	Aki-nada	3.5
13 Oct 20	Hachijom..	4.6	18 Oct 20	HokubuTo..	3.1
			18 Oct 20	Oki Miyagi	3.7

Perform steps a) through f) from problem 2 above.

7. News services and scientific agencies have projected a possible off-shore earthquake on the Pacific Northwest coast. This raises concerns over potential Tsunami effects in low lying coastal areas. The table below documents world wide historical data regarding Tsunami height. (6)(source Wikipedia article "List of Tsunamis", Creative Commons Attribution-ShareAlike 3.0 Unported License)(see https://creativecommons.org/licenses/by-sa/3.0/)

Date	Location	Height (m)	Date	Location	Height (m)
1605	Nankai	9	1960	Hilo Hawaii	11
1707	Nankai	10	1964	Alaska	30
1755	Lisbon Port.	15	1983	Sea of Japan	10
1771	Okinawa	30	1992	Nicaragua	10
1781	Pingtung	30	1993	Hokaido	31
1782	Shimabara	100	1998	Papau NG	15
1854	Nankai	8	1999	Sea Mamara	3
1867	US VI	8	2004	Indian Ocea	33

1868	Hawaii	18	2006	South Java	6
1883	Krakatoa	40	2007	Solomon	12
1896	Sanriku	30	2009	Samoa	14
1905	Ecuador	5	2011	Japan Coast	41
1906	Ecuador	5	2011	New Zealand	4
1923	Kanto	12	2013	Solomon	1
1929	Newfoundland	7	2015	Chile	5
1933	Sanriku	10	2017	Greenland	90
1934	Tafjord Norway	62	2018	Sulawesei	2
1956	Amorgos Greece	30			

Perform steps a) through f) from problem 2 above.

END OF HOMEWORK SECTION 1

CONTINUE CH 5 On Next Page

Chapter 5: Discard Data and Need for Failure Count Adjustment:

Discarded data points often occur during laboratory testing. They result from two issues.

- Test sample removal prior to planned end of test (due to laboratory facility failures.)

- Sample item failure by some mechanism other than test targeted mechanism/s.

If an unfailed test specimen is removed at known test time, then the removal time is Discard Data; and, some credit is due for the time it did survive. While Discard Data is not treated like other data-points, adjustments are made to failure counts of other data-points to achieve unbiased population modeling. Let's look at why this idea makes sense. Consider the following hypothetical situation. A test is begun with six "visually identical" widgets.

- At 25% of intended test duration: Widget #1 fails.

- At 30% : Widgets #2 & #3 are removed due to test chamber problems.

- At 65% : Widget #4 fails.

When sample #1 failed, six test articles represented the widget population. When sample #4 failed, only 3 samples represented the population. If the test had continued to include the missing 3 widgets, wouldn't you expect additional failure/s? Considering the number of samples at risk, doesn't it make sense that failure #2 should be double-counted?

- Failures represent some percentage of the population, based on data-set sequence position. Mid-test reduction of data-sample count upsets the effective sequence position, thus requiring some kind of adjustment to credited failure increment.

- Doesn't it make sense that a single failure of a data-set reduced to 3 total items should count about the same as two failures from the original data-set of 6 items?

- Thoughtful consideration can refine the "adjusted rank" number; but, the argument presented is sufficient to explain the need for adjusting failure increment.

Formalized analysis techniques soon justify the following conclusion: The failure increment for the previously described test becomes (1 new failure) * (5/3) = 1.67 increase in lieu of simply adding one more failure. The failure sequence thus becomes 1st failure followed by 2.67th failure (see Eq 5-3 below for adjusted increment equation). While counter intuitive, discards usually result in fractional failure numbers.

The next section compares three failure rank adjustment methods. All three give similar results. The Bompas-Smith model is based on linear adjustment to failure count increment as discussed above. The AVCO/LYCOMING modified Johnson Equation is based on probability of a Discard's true failure occurring between subsequent failure points. The Weibull Risk Adjusted Rank (AKA Watson's-Weibull Adjusted Rank) allocates future failure probability of Discard data-points to subsequent failures based on Weibull Risk Equations. While awkward to use, Watson's-Weibull Adjusted Rank method is implements well justified mathematics and is thus the standard of excellence.

Rank Order Adjustment Methods:

Below, methods to compute Adjusted Rank (i.e. discard adjusted) from failure sequence are presented. Concepts for why these methods work are presented in Appendix K.

- N = original data-set size (for tests, the number of articles put into test)

- Prior Adj. Rank = adjusted rank (i.e. adjusted fail order no) of previous failure.

- Contra Order = backwards count from last data-point (items remaining in test)

- Recent Failures = count of failures after immediately prior recorded failure.

- Fail Rank Increment = additional failures to be credited to cumulative failure count. (This is usually a decimal number such as 1.25 in lieu of 1)

Bompas-Smith Linear Correction for Rank Increment (7):

Eq 5-3: Failure Rank Increment=RecentFailures*(N − Prior Adj. Rank)/(Contra Order)

AVCO/LYCOMING modified Johnson Rank Adjustment (8):

Eq 5-4: Adj Rank = [(Contra Order) * (Prior Adj Rank) + (N+1)] / [(Contra Order)+1]

Watson's-Weibull Adjusted Ranks:

Watson's Weibull Adjusted Rank method does not have a closed form solution and can only be used as a computer algorithm employing a two step process. In the first step, Weibull β and η are estimated. In the second step, estimated values of β and η are used to compute future failure probability for each Discard data-point to support rank adjustments of succeeding failure points. The method is fully explained in Chapter 8 and is implemented by the Watson-Weibull program.

The astute reader may wonder how the three methods would differ, if applied to the same problem. The notional data-set below is synthetic (a computer creation based on a known Weibull distribution) and is the basis for such a comparison. Note: Table below is "double columned".

Notional Tire Tread Wear-out Life in Miles (Beta=2.25, Eta=40000 miles)

Order	Miles	Discards	Order	Miles	Discards
1	12827		6	33987	
2	13000	D	7	44130	
3	24719		8	50772	
4	29401		9	61136	
5	30000	D			

Table 5-4: Tire Tread Life

Table 5-5 below presents the adjusted rank (adjusted fail order) number as computed by each of the methods discussed. The Bompas-Smith method has an extra column, because the method computes the increment which must be added to the previous adjusted rank number to get a value comparable to the right two columns.

The column at the far left, is the raw sequence (ordinal) number for each of the data-points, irrespective of whether they were failure vs. discarded data points.

	Bompas-Smith Increment	Bompas-Smith AdjRank	Avo/Lycoming AdjRank	Watson-Weib Adj Rank
1	1	1	1	1
2	D	D	D	D
3	1.143	2.143	2.125	2.188
4	1.143	3.286	3.250	3.285
5	D	D	D	D
6	1.429	4.715	4.600	4.507
7	1.429	6.143	5.950	6.022
8	1.429	7.572	7.300	7.309
9	1.429	9.000	8.650	8.642

Table 5-5: Comparison of Rank Adjustment Method Results

Which is the Best Method?

Results of Watson's Weibull Adjusted Rank method should be regarded as definitive, because the method is based on well founded mathematics but it is not of practical use (because it can only be implemented as a computer algorithm). Comparison of all three methods shows little difference in rank adjustment result. The Bompas-Smith method produces results comparable to the Avo/Lycoming (modified Leonard Jones) method. For real world analysis, either method may be used.

Watson's Weibull Adjusted Rank method cannot be expressed as a closed form equation, and is thus not practical for everyday use.

Chapter 5 Part 2: Discard Data & Characterizing Populations:

Chapter 5 Part 2 will now explain how to determine β and η for data-sets which include discards. This process is like that already covered with the following exceptions:

- The Watson Weibull Standard Template for data-sets with discards will be used in lieu of the previous one. Different "blacked out" columns will steer you through additional steps to compute the needed and adjusted rank numbers.

- Adjusted rank numbers may be determined by either the Bompas-Smith, or the Avo/ Lycoming rank adjustment methods just described.

Aside from using adjusted rank values (in lieu of raw Rank values used previously), the Weibull Plot and determination of β and η are determined as before.

Example: Characterization of Data-set with Discards:

Tire sales are often accompanied by a prorated warranty that compensates the purchaser for premature wear-out. Consider a tire manufacturer who performs road tests of tires to determine tread-life distribution. A total of 9 tires were tested with results as follows.

Cyclops Tyre Company   Purpose: Eval Normal Wear

Tire Model: Hermes Super-Fast All Weather Z9000   Report Date:

Sample No	Mileage	Comment
1	24719	Normal tread wear-out
2	50772	Normal tread wear-out
3	13000	Belt Separation
4	61136	Normal tread wear-out
5	44130	Normal tread wear-out
6	112827	Normal tread wear-out
7	33987	Normal tread wear-out
8	29401	Normal tread wear-out
9	30000	Sidewall damage-vandalism

Table 5-6: Tire Tread-life Data with Discards

The Tire Analysis in Three Steps:

1. Document sorted data-set using Watson Standard Template with discards.

2. Use a spreadsheet to establish pseudo X,Y plotting values for a Weibull Plot.

3. Create Weibull Plot. Determine β and η that correspond to the data. Determine R^2

Step 1: Document data using Watson Standard Template (or spreadsheet equivalent)

-   "Order" and "Data Value" Columns: Enter sorted data values. Don't sort "Order".

-   Adj. Rank Column, Eq 3-4: AdjRank=[(ContraOrder*PriorAdjRank)+(N+1)]/ [ContraOrder+1]

-   Median Column: Use Benard's Equation: Median% = (AdjRank-.3)/(N+.4)

Watson Standard Template- for Data with Discards   Test Description: Tire Test

Number of Samples: N=9   Test Date:

Order	Contra	DataVal	Discard	Rank	AdjRank	Median
1	9	12827		BLANK	1	.0745
2	8	13000	D	BLANK	D	D
3	7	24719		BLANK	2.125	.1941
4	6	29401		BLANK	3.25	.3138
5	5	30000	D	BLANK	D	D
6	4	33987		BLANK	4.600	.4574
7	3	44130		BLANK	5.950	.6011
8	2	50772		BLANK	7.300	.7447
9	1	61136		BLANK	8.650	.8883

Table 5-7: Watson Standard Template with Discards

Step 2: Make pseudo x & y value spreadsheet to support a Weibull Plot (Column E & F).

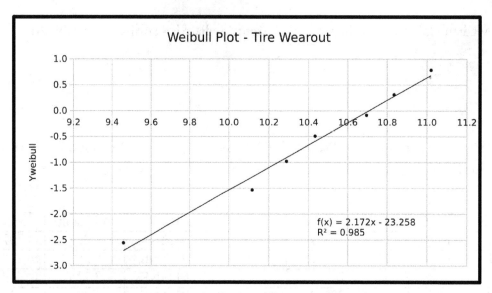

	A	B	C	D	E	F
1		AdjRank	Value	Median	Ln(Value)	LnLn(1/(1-Med%))
2	1	1.000	12827	9.46%	9.4593	-2.3089
3	2	2.125	24719	22.97%	10.1153	-1.3432
4	3	3.250	29401	36.49%	10.2888	-0.7898
5	4	4.600	33987	50.00%	10.4337	-0.3665
6	5	5.950	44130	63.51%	10.6949	0.0082
7	6	7.300	50772	77.03%	10.8351	0.3858
8	7	8.650	61136	90.54%	11.0209	0.8579

Figure 5-8: Spreadsheet to Support Weibull Plot

Step 3: Use spreadsheet columns E & F to graph a Weibull Plot

Figure 5-9: Weibull Plot of Tire Tread Life

Example Report Discussion: "The Weibull Plot exhibits data-points closely fitting the straight line which is consistent with the very good R^2 value 98.5%. Examination of the data-points shows no evidence of curvature which often indicates the need for three parameter Weibull Analysis. While a data-set having a greater number of points would add confidence, the Weibull Plot above indicates a Weibull 2 parameter model is appropriate."

Comment: This example was based on a computer generated data-set. We thus know the underlying data was built using a Weibull equation having $\beta=2.2$ and $\eta=40000$. The close approximation ($\beta=2.17$ and $\eta=44716$) to the original data-set parameters indicates the modified Leonard Jones rank adjustment provided excellent compensation for the two discarded data-points. Leonard Jones is not always so effective.

Weibull Equations for PDF and CDF Plots:

The general form for the Weibull PDF was provided by Equation 5-1. The particular Weibull Equation corresponding to this data-set can be created by substituting values ($\beta=2.17$ and $\eta=44716$) into the general PDF Weibull Equation.

If desired, a spreadsheet can be used to create a Weibull PDF graph for the tire example. This is best done by spreadsheet. In column A, insert regularly spaced x values beginning with .01 and increasing in steps to about two times η (Do not use actual data-points). Column B is computed from the particular PDF equation based on values from Column A.

When this is complete, "high-light" Columns A and B. Issue an X-Y graph command from the spreadsheet. The spreadsheet should create something that looks like one of the curves from Figure 5-4. If errors result, or the graph looks very strange, see Note below.

Note: The Weibull PDF equation is long and tricky. It is easy to make a mistake and this usually results in some kind of spreadsheet error message. It is often difficult to find your error. If this happens, try using several columns with each computing part of the equation. In the final column on the right, multiply the various columns together for the overall result. This is helpful because when you are getting all zeros instead of reasonable y values, you can easily spot the part of your equation that is resulting in zeros and needs fixing and likewise if your are getting "out of range" errors.

The various procedures (depending on number of data points, suspension or not, etc.) often makes a "muddle" of our understanding. Often, the student wastes time computing something that is really not needed for the current problem. To clarify what should be done, the Chapter Summary provides an example worked out, which shows the "flow of numbers" from data sheet to worksheet to equation. The example shows creation of the Weibull Plot and finally determines the values of β and η.

Chapter 5 Part 1 Summary:

Important methods have been demonstrated: 1) Routine Weibull Plot creation for data-sets without Discards. 2) Determination of Weibull parameter values for β and η based on Weibull Plots. 3) Modified method when Discard Data is present. Examples follow:

Ch 5 Summary: Weibull Analysis WITHOUT Discards

Test Data Sheet

Table 5-8

Test Sample No	Measured Data
1	10.41
2	17.47
3	24.38
4	33.90
N=4	

Watson Template

W/O Discards

Table 5-9

Order	Contra	Data	Discard	Rank	AdjRank	Median
1	Blank	10.41	Blank	1	Blank	
2	Blank	17.47	Blank	2	Blank	
3	Blank	24/38	Blank	3	Blank	
4	Blank	33.90	Blank	4	Blank	

Weibull Plot Spreadsheet

Figure 5-10

	Rank	Data	Med%	Ln(Data)	LnLn(1/(1-Med%)))
1					
2	1	10.41	0.1591	2.3428	-1.7529
3	2	17.47	0.3864	2.8605	-0.7167
4	3	24.38	0.6136	3.1938	-0.0503
5	4	33.90	0.8409	3.5234	0.6088

Weibull Plot

Figure 5-11

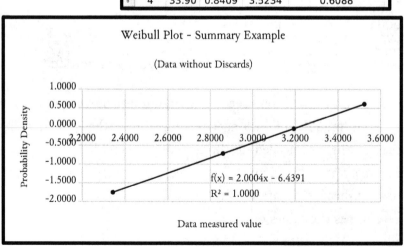

Weibull Plot - Summary Example

(Data without Discards)

$f(x) = 2.0004x - 6.4391$

$R^2 = 1.0000$

$\beta = 2.0004$

$\eta = e^{-(-6.439/2.004)}$

94

Ch 5 Summary: Weibull Analysis WITH Discards

Test Data Set

Table 5-10

Test Sample No	Measured Data	Discard?
1	10.41	
2	12.00	D
3	17.47	
4	33.90	
N=4		

Discards: [(ContraOrder * PriorAdj)+(N+1)]/[ContraOrder+1] = Adj Rank (e.g. 2.333)

Compute Adjusted Rank Using Bold Cells Below

Table 5-11

Order	ContraOrder	Data	Discard	Rank	AdjRank	Median
1	4	10.41		Blank	**1**	
2	3	12.00	D	Blank	D	
3	**2**	17.47		Blank	**2.333**	
4	1	33.90		Blank	3.667	
N=4						

Weibull Spreadsheet

Figure 5-12

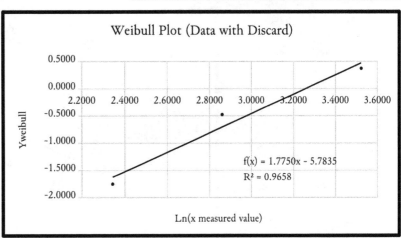

Weibull Plot (Discard)

Figure 5-13

$\beta = 1.775$

$\eta = e^\wedge-(-5.784/1.775)$

95

Ch 5 Summary: Weibull Analysis WITH Runout Discard

Test Data Sheet

Table 5-12

Test Sample No	Measured Data	Discard?
1	9.32	
2	10.00	D
3	15.37	
4	26.88	
5	30.00	D
N=5		

[(ContraOrder*PriorAdj)+(N+1)]/[ContraOrder+1] = AdjRank (e.g. 2.25)

Table 5-13

Order	ContraOrd	DataValue	Discard	Rank	AdjRank	Median
1	5	9.32		1	1	
2	4	10.00	D			
3	3	15.37		2	2.25	4
4	2	26.88		3	3.50	
5	1	30.00	D			
N=5						

Weibull Spreadsheet

Figure 5-14

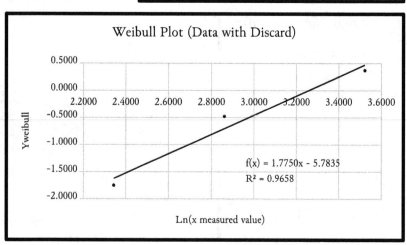

Weibull Plot

Figure 5-15

$\beta=1.775$

$\eta = e\wedge-(-5.78/1.78)$

96

Three preceding examples were provided to show how analysis should be done; however, a quick review of the accuracy achieved is also instructive.

For the first two examples, I created raw data based on a Weibull Equation with $\beta=2$ and $\eta=25$. We thus have "god like" knowledge of the answer which can be compared to analysis results.

When there are no discarded data-points and a data-set is of very high quality, good results can be expected. Chapter 5 summary Example 1 correctly identified $\beta=2$ and $\eta=25$.

When discards are present, a best estimate is all that can be expected from Weibull Analysis, because there are several possible "god's view" solutions which might represent truth. Summary Example 2 estimated $\beta=1.78$ and $\eta=26$ in lieu of the correct values $\beta=2$ and $\eta=25$.

For the third example, a data-point was added at the end, and we do not know the "god's view" answer, however our solution $\beta=1.78$ and $\eta=26$ seems likely correct as the Adjusted Rank for the 3rd actual failure should somewhat reduce the Weibull plot line slope.

During actual analysis, data-sets should be much larger than 5 data-points, and results usually improve. Despite our rather small data-set, all three examples produce results that range between reasonable estimates and accurate results.

Should Available Discard Data Always be Used?

Yes, discard data, when present, should be used. Predictions made by ignoring discard information are far less satisfactory than analysis which includes it.

A Common Mistake:

Given the complexity of Weibull Distribution characterization, it is easy to make a mistake. One of the more common mistakes is the belief that suspensions beyond the last failure make no difference. This is wrong. N represents all the samples that were exposed to the test environment, and each of those samples is correlated via the Median Percent to the underlying population. If we test 25 samples, but stop our N value at failure point 5, then we will be incorrectly spreading our first five data points from 12.96% to 87.06% of population values. The correct analysis spreads these five points from roughly 2.8% to 18.5% given that 20 more data-points represent the portion of population beyond the 5th failure.

Chapter Footnotes:

1. Concrete Strength Characterization - Public Domain: Comparison of the Compressive Strength of Concrete made with Limestone Screenings vs. Torpedo Sand, F. B. Whitney, Thesis submitted to President and Faculty of Armour Institute of Technology, Chicago Illinois, 1905

2. Kochi Japan Rainfall: The Japan Meteorological Agency. See authorization Appendix N.

3. Annual U.S. Flu Infections: from CDC website. See conditions of use Appendix N.

4. Annual Cotton Yield: from USDA website. See conditions of use Appendix N.

5. Japan Earthquakes: The Japan Meteorological Agency. Use authorization Appendix N.

6. Tsunamis off the NW Coast: From Wikipedia. See use authorization Appendix N.

7. Bompas-Smith Adjusted Rank Equation: Equation presented is based on Mechanical Survival by J. H. Bompas-Smith Chapter 2. The exact expression is a modification of Bompas-Smith's original work.

8. Modified Johnson Adjusted Rank Equation: Obtained from The New Weibull Handbook, written and copyright by Robert B. Abernethy 1993

9. Rivet Strength Data – Public Domain from : National Advisory Committee for Aeronautics, Wartime Report- Tests on Hydraulically Expanded Rivets, Langley Field Virginia ,1944

10. Cannon Bore Erosion- Public Domain: from the US Journal of Artillery 1892 - 1903.

11. Liberty Ship Fates: Wikipedia article under Creative Commons Attribution – Share Alike License.

12. Queensland Shark Catch Data is available from the Queensland Government web site, and is distributed with a Public Commons license. See Appendix N for terms of usage.

Homework Chapter 5 Section 2: Weibull Data with Discard Data

WWII Rivet Tests (Public Domain – (9)): WWII Wartime Reports were issued to address engineering properties of various manufacturing techniques. An important issue was the strength of aluminum aircraft rivets. Tests were run to determine:

- Shear strength of 100 degree countersunk .125 diameter rivets. Thickness of joined aluminum plates was 5/64 inch thick.

- Tensile strength of 100 degree countersunk .125 diameter rivets. Joined aluminum plates were 5/64 inch thick.

- Pulsating shear strength of round head .125 rivets: Loading was 15# continuous plus pulsating shear. The "x variable of interest" was stress cycles to failure.

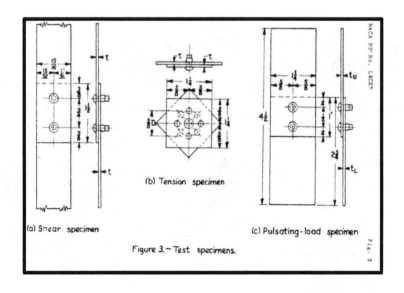

(b) Tension specimen

(a) Shear specimen

(c) Pulsating-load specimen

Figure 3.~Test specimens.

99

1. Rivet shear strength results are provide in the table below.

- Use Appendix B template. Document data sample. Analyze the primary failure mode.

- Make a table & spreadsheet to create a Weibull Plot (Table 5-10, 5-11 & Fig 5-12)

- Using a spreadsheet, create a Weibull Plot (see Figure 5-13)

- Determine β, η and R^2.

Sample No	ShearFailForce	FailMode
S1	339 lbs	Expansion Fracture
S2	315 lbs	Shear
S3	307 lbs	Shear
S4	320 lbs	Shear
S5	311 lbs	Shear
S6	312 lbs	Shear
S7	327 lbs	Shear
S8	328 lbs	Shear

2. Rivet tensile strength test results for .125 countersunk rivets are provided in the table below (9). Do steps shown in problem 1 using data from table below.

Sample No	ShearFailForce	FailMode
T1	157 lbs	Shank pull through plates
T2	152 lbs	Tension fail of hollow shank
T3	180 lbs	Tension fail of hollow shank
T4	121 lbs	Shank pull through plates
T5	153 lbs	Shank pull through plates
T6	155 lbs	Shank pull through plates
T7	116 lbs	Shank pull through plates
T8	96 lbs	Shank pull through plates

3. Rivet pulsating load test results are provided in table below (9). Do steps shown in problem 1 using the data from table below.

Sample No	Cycles to Fail
P1	40
P2	20
P3	30
P4	30
P5	70
P6	30

4. During the 1890s, nitroglycerin based smokeless powder replaced the older and less powerful black power. The smokeless powder burned at higher temperatures and rapidly eroded cannon barrels thus limiting their life. The following Public Domain data was extracted from US Journal of Artillery for the period 1892 to 1903. (10)

Do steps shown in problem 1 to characterize the life of cannon barrels subjected to smokeless powder. Use data from table below. Write a ¼ paragraph discussing the resultant Weibull Plot and whether the Plot seems to support use of Weibull for this problem.

Size in	Rounds	Gun Mfr	Data Source	Fail Mode
2.25	472	Unknown	JUSA1895 p739	Bore Wear
10	275	Crozier Wire	JUSA 1903 p8	Bore Wear
8	390	Watervliet	JUSA 1903 p13	Bore Wear
8	355	Westpoint	Ditto	Bore Wear
8	388	Wespoint	Ditto	Barrel cracks
10	281	Watervliet	Ditto	Bore Wear
12	265	Watervliet	Ditto	Bore Wear
12 Mortar	398	Unkown	Ditto	Bore Wear
12 Mortar	399	Unknown	Dito	Bore Wear

5. Cargo Ships (Source Wikipedia. Liberty Ships (11) under Creative Commons Attribution-Share A like License) During WWII, a huge number of Liberty Cargo ships were built to transport war materials to combat areas. The following table documents a sample of 22 ships, tabulating their age and fate. Your task is determine whether Weibull can describe the age at "scrapping." Also, determine β, η and R^2 .

Use Appendix B template to document the data sample. Analyze primary failure mode.

- Make spreadsheet table to support creation of a Weibull Plot (Tables 5-10 & 5-11)

- Using a spreadsheet, create a Weibull Plot (see Figure 5-12 & 5-13)

- Evaluate the Weibull Plot to determine if Weibull adequately describes this data-set.

- Determine β, η and R^2. Document all of the above and submit to Instructor.

Ship	Age	Fate	Ship	Age	Fate
SS Hammond	20	Scrapped	SS AHamilton	21	Scrapped
SS F Lever	25	Scrapped	SS Bell	20	Scrapped
SS Cassatt	21	Scrapped	SS A Macomb	5	Torpedoed
SS Cermak	21	Scrapped	SS A Majors	29	Scrapped
SS Mils	28	Scrapped	SS A Wilson	9	Scrapped
SS Abe Baldwin	35	Reefed	SS Al Dupoint	26	Scrapped
SS Rosenbert	18	Sunk	SS A Palmer	.5	Torpedoed
SSAda Rehan	24	Scrapped	SS Al Johnson	14	Scrapped
SS A Seeger	25	Collision	SS A Bierce	15	Scrapped
SS Gallatin	3	Torpedoed	SS A Curtin	1	Torpedoed
SS A Ryder	23	Scrapped	SS Huntington	27	Abandoned

6. Based on the Cyclops Tyre Company (see Chapter 5 Table 5-6 and Figure 5-9)

- Write the PDF equation for the data-set

- Using a spreadsheet, graph the PDF equation

102

Chapter 6: Weibull Equations & Analysis Methods

Chapter Goals:

Chapter 6 introduces the Weibull equations accompanied by graphs. The 2 parameter Weibull is a simplification of the more general 3 parameter Weibull. We will cover the following:

- Physical meaning of the shape parameter β.

- Physical meaning of the scale parameter η.

- Justification of the Weibull Plot (graphic trend-line analysis) method of Chapter 3.

- An Example of the 3 Parameter Weibull Plot Problem

- Note: The location parameter will be called xo or Xo interchangeably in Chapter 6.

The following pages display the Weibull Equations (both PDF and CDF) and show what their graphs look like. Both the 2 parameter and the 3 parameter Weibull will be shown.

The Three Parameter Weibull Equations and their Graphs:

Eq 6-1

$$PDF - 3parameter: f(x) = \left(\beta \cdot \frac{(X - Xo)^{(\beta - 1)}}{(\eta^\beta)} \right) \cdot \frac{1}{e^{\left(\left(\frac{(X - Xo)}{\eta}\right)^\beta\right)}}$$

Eq 6-2

$$CDF - 3parameter: F(x) = 1 - \frac{1}{e^{\left(\left(\frac{(X - Xo)}{\eta}\right)^\beta\right)}}$$

There are two important three parameter Weibull Equations. They are the probability density function (or PDF) and the cumulative density function (or CDF). As discussed previously, the CDF represents probability as the area under the PDF curve. The CDF enables direct computation of probability (from x=0 to x=a) by substituting value "a" in lieu of x and performing the calculation. (Of course Beta, Eta and Xo must also be known.)

The corresponding 2 parameter Weibull Equations (PDF and CDF) are derived by simply replacing Xo by zero (and thus Xo totally disappears from the equations). These equations are documented by Eq 6-3 and 6-4 below.

PDF graphs are presented in Figure 6-1 below for both 3 parameter and 2 parameter Weibull equations (for several different β values).

The 3 parameter Weibull equation has shape parameter β, scale parameter η and the location parameter Xo. The effect of β, η & Xo are as shown; but may be summarized as:

- β determines the basic shape of the PDF.

- Xo determines how far the PDF shape is offset to the right.

- While not illustrated, η determines how much the PDF is stretched horizontally.

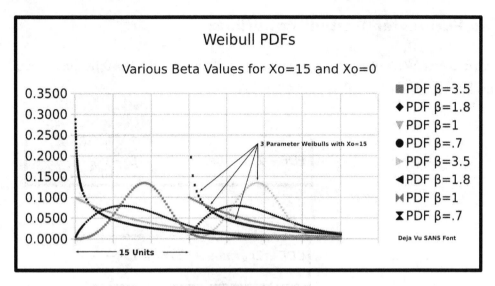

- Figure 6-1: Effect of Xo in 3 parameter Weibull

Visual examination of Figure 6-1 will confirm the following:

- The 3 parameter Weibull has an Xo position parameter while the 2 parameter Weibull does not. When Xo=15, the PDF graph will be shifted 15 units to the right. The 3 parameter Weibull has an x domain beginning at Xo. The 2 parameter Weibull begins at the origin (i.e. x = 0).

- Shape parameter β determines the basic shape of the Weibull, and has the same effect on both 3 parameter and 2 parameter Weibull PDFs.

- The scale parameter η is the X position representing 63.2% of the PDF area. Thus, the effect of increasing η is to horizontally stretch the PDF. This is true for both 3 parameter and 2 parameter Weibull PDFs and regardless of β and Xo values.

105

The Two Parameter Weibull Equations:

The two parameter Weibull equations may be derived by setting Xo = 0 in the three parameter equations. The result for both PDF and CDF follows:

Eq 6-3

$$PDF - 2parameter: f(x) = \left(\beta \cdot \frac{x^{(\beta-1)}}{(\eta^\beta)} \right) \cdot \frac{1}{e^{\left(\left(\frac{x}{\eta} \right)^\beta \right)}}$$

Eq 6-4

$$CDF - 2parameter: F(x) = 1 - \frac{1}{e^{\left(\left(\frac{x}{\eta} \right)^\beta \right)}}$$

When Should 3 vs. the 2 Parameter Weibull be Used?

Initial analysis should be performed with a 2 parameter Weibull Analysis. If a viable 3 parameter analysis capability is readily available, the 3 parameter solution should always be tried and the results compared both visually and by review of R^2. The 3 parameter Weibull solution should be used when any of the following conditions occur.

- R^2 value for 3 parameter is much better than R^2 for 2 parameter solution.

- The 3 parameter solution eliminates "arc curvature" of data-points.

- The 3 parameter solution significantly addresses data-point "end drupe".

The 2 parameter solution should be used when:

- Xo offset parameter of 3 parameter is nearly zero.

- Only spreadsheet analysis is available, thus precluding effective 3 parameter analysis.

The above recommendations are made based on the following:

A spreadsheet is not realistically capable of performing an adequate and convenient 3 parameter analysis. For users who do not have a good 3 parameter analysis capability (commercial Weibull software), Chapter 7 includes discussion of "arced data-points about the fit line," which is the best means of identifying need for 3 parameter analysis. This observational approach is problematic because even slight "data-point arc" can significantly affect determined values of β and η and it is difficult to detect slight arcs in the presence of data scatter.

There are also circumstances where a 3 parameter Weibull should be expected. The 3 parameter Weibull Equation applies when onset of a phenomena begins at some value other than zero. One well known example is metal fatigue, where samples only begin to fail after thousands of cycles. We can imagine other examples. There is likely some "smallest size of shark" that is biologically viable, thus suggesting need for 3 parameter analysis.

Accurate determination of β, η and Xo are important for several reasons.

- Future predictions are very sensitive to Beta.

- Determination of equipment Mean Time Between Failures is sensitive to β and η

- Determination of failure onset for equipment requires determination of Xo

The Reason analysts are fond of the 2 parameter Weibull is that Chapter 5 methods directly determine β and η while a 3 parameter Weibull Analysis requires trial and error solution.

An example using real data is the most convincing way of showing the reader that 2 parameter analysis applied to a 3 parameter population can utterly misrepresent a population. The following example is based on United Nations agricultural data for Japanese tea yields (tons per hectare).

Issues raised in the forgoing paragraphs (arced data, R^2 etc.) are well illustrated by this real life example.

107

Comparison of Data Analysis 3 Parameter vs. 2 Parameter.

Based on Japanese Tea productivity data, the following graphs are presented:

- Yearly trend graph

- 2 Parameter Weibull Plot

- 3 Parameter Weibull Plot

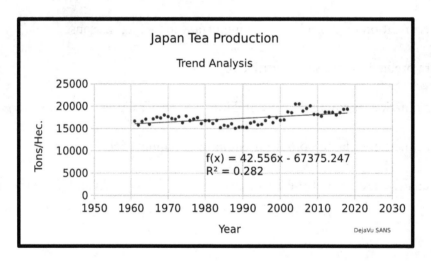

Figure 6-2: Japanese Tea Production Trend

Yearly trend shows slight increases of tea tons/hectare. Scatter compared to the rise is not clearly dominant thus bringing legitimacy of statistical analysis into question; however, we shall proceed without further correction to the analysis.

The 2 parameter and 3 parameter Weibull Plots follow:

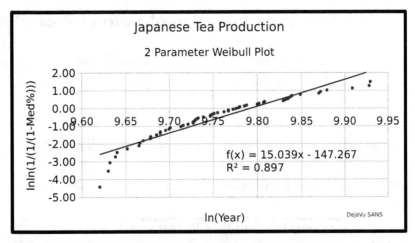

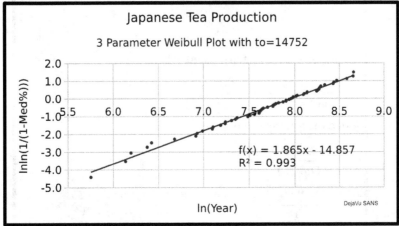

Figures 6-3 & 6-4: Weibull Plots as Noted

The 2 parameter (upper) Weibull Plot exhibits "arced data points" which often indicates need for a 3 parameter Weibull. Indicated β and η are 15 and 17900 respectively. The very high β value at 15 further hints something is wrong with analysis or data.

The 3 parameter (lower) Weibull Plot was performed by trial and error to identify Xo=14752 (which subtracts from x values before Weibull Plot creation). After analyzing the Xo reduced data using the 3 parameter method, straight line conformance of data points is achieved. The β value has reduced from 15 to a realistic 1.865 and the R^2 fit measure indicates 99.3% in lieu of the rather poor 89.7% of the 2 parameter Weibull.

Why Does Weibull Plot Determination of Beta and Eta Work?

The justification for assignment of β and η based on the Weibull Plot follows. The approach is justified by algebraic manipulation of the Weibull CDF equation that forces a linear equation in terms of pseudo variables:

Ypseudo = Ln(Ln(1/(1-Cum%))). Cum% is data point Median%.

Xpseudo = Ln(x). Calculation is performed for each data-set x value. Likewise for Cum%

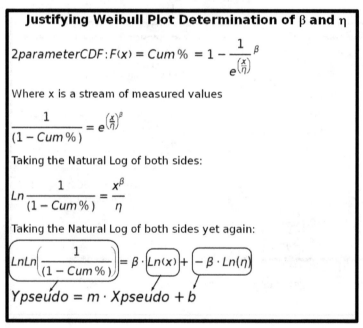

Figure 6-5: Justifying Weibull Plot

From the proof above, it follows that:

- Xpseudo=Ln(x)   x is a measured data-point value

- Ypseudo = Ln(Ln(1/(1-Cum%)))   Cum% is the Median Percent of a data-point

- $-\beta * Ln(\eta)$ must equal the y intercept of the fitted Weibull Plot line which enables solution of η once the Weibull Line equation is known.

110

Discussion:

It is common in math to replace a cluster of variables by a new variable name, to simplify so that we can understand what the math is saying. I will use the following substitutions and reasoning:

- Ypseudo=Ln(Ln(1/(1-Med%))). We want a y axis variable that somehow represents Median Percent. Figure 6-5 suggests this substitution, computed for each data point.

- Xpseudo=Ln(x). Ideally, we would like the x axis to represent the measured data-point value. But Figure 6-5 indicates using Ln(x) will force a linear equation with slope β. To use this, it requires us to replace all data-point x values with the natural log of those values (i.e. Ln(x)). Note: We are lucky to have a useful variable cluster that only involves the x variable!

- A data-set is a sorted collection of measured values. Each value corresponds to a Median Percent (recall Benard's Equation). So we have a collection of N pairs of numbers (x,med%) and we can convert each of these pairs into pseudo x and pseudo y values (before doing the Weibull Plot and finding the best fit line.)

- We use the N pseudo data pairs (Xpseudo, Ypseudo) to create a Weibull Plot that puts a best straight line equation through the points. If we are using a spreadsheet, this is done in the graphing mode by inserting a "trend line" type linear. A spreadsheet can also display the equation in the form y=mx+b.

- Next convert from m and b back to values β and η. β = m. The value of η = e^-(b/m). This last conversion may be derived from b = - β * Ln(η) evident in Figure 6-5.

While the process is lengthy to explain, it hopefully brings clarity to the compact mathematical notation presented by Figure 6-5.

Conclusion: Figure 6-5 justifies using a sorted data-set to compute pseudo x corresponding to each data-point. We simply take the natural log of the x values. Ypseudo corresponding to each data-point is based on Median Percent of each data point. It also follows that:

- β is the slope of the Weibull Plot line. (i.e. β = m)

- η can be calculated as e^(-b/m) where m is again the slope of the Weibull Plot line. A scientific calculator makes quick work of the calculation.

Figure 6-6 below illustrates how the Weibull Plot and axes are related, based on the pseudo variables. The reader should take note that if x=η , then 63% of the population will have been trapped between that value and the origin.

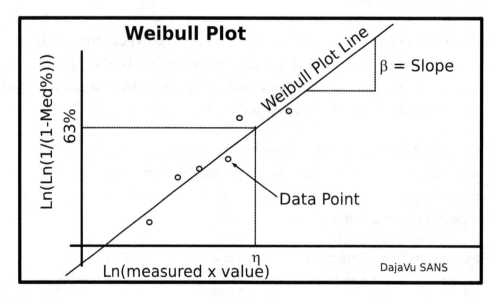

Figure 6-6: Weibull Plot with Key Features

We are familiar with the "average value" which conceptually is the "balance point" for a carefully "cut out" PDF. The median is the x value below which 50% of data-points in a population exist. But there is still another parameter for Weibull distributions that is similar. Parameter η ALWAYS represents 63% of Weibull population no matter the value of β.

Why Does x=η Always Trap 63% of the Weibull Population?

It is perhaps odd that scale factor η, represents 63.2% of the population regardless of the value of β and the consequent changes in shape of the PDF. The following algebra based on Equation 6-4 leads to this conclusion.

Beginning with the CDF:

Eq 6-5

$$2parameterCDF : F(x) = Cum\% = 1 - \frac{1}{e^{\left(\left(\frac{x}{\eta}\right)^{\beta}\right)}}$$

If x= η:

Eq 6-6

$$Cum\% = 1 - \frac{1}{e^{\left(\left(\frac{\eta}{\eta}\right)^{\beta}\right)}} = 1 - \frac{1}{e} = 63.21\%$$

We are still left wondering "How does the Weibull twist and turn to make this possible?" The CDF below enables the reader to simply read up from x to determine the cumulative percent of population. It also demonstrates how x=η always indicates 63% of population.

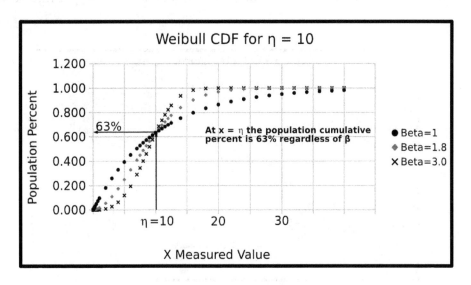

Figure 6-7: x=Eta => 63% of Population

Developing "Gut Feel" for Weibull Parameters:

The skill to extract useful information from Weibull equations is important but not enough. The analyst needs a visceral understanding of what the equation is communicating and especially how parameters β and η influence the message. While parameter effects apply to all Weibulls, the discussion below will be framed in terms of equipment failures. As presented earlier, the 2 parameter Weibull PDF Equation is:

Eq 6-7
$$PDF - 2parameter: f(x) = \left(\beta \cdot \frac{x^{(\beta-1)}}{(\eta^\beta)} \right) \cdot \frac{1}{e^{\left(\frac{x}{\eta}\right)^\beta}}$$

Weibull Analysis can be applied to many phenomena. One Weibull application is the description of the percentage machines failing with increasing age. For this application, the area under the curve computed by Eq 6-7 would describe the failed percentage at whatever age x you may choose. The shape of the Weibull PDF (and failure behavior) is strongly affected by parameter β . The graph below shows how changing β from .8 to 1 to 3 affects the equipment failure PDF. If β is less than 1, many machines will fail soon after being put into service.

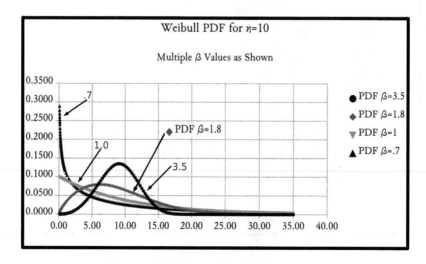

Figure 6-8: Variation of Shape with β

From Figure 6-8 above, we can infer the following (1):

- $\beta < 1$ is associated with large numbers of early product life failures. This pattern is called infant mortality and "usually results in customer dissatisfaction".

- $\beta=1$ is associated with a constant failure tendency throughout the product life. The behavior is called a constant hazard rate and is associated with products who's failure tendency is not age dependent.

- $\beta>1$: Indicates wear-out failure. This means that newly delivered product rarely fails, however as age or usage increases, Failures begin and gradually increase. Eventually, most of the product will have already failed, and total number of failures decreases.

The three Beta categories above often indicate various equipment failure causes during design and manufacture. When a Weibull distribution is based on a single failure mode, the categories above have distinct implications for both customer satisfaction and equipment management. But when a Weibull distribution describes a mixture of failure modes, generalizations based on β are doubtful.

- When Weibull indicates infant mortality (i.e. $\beta<1$), the most active period of failure begins when the equipment goes into service and gradually decreases as equipment ages. Infant mortality is often associated with poor process control, or with processes that are inherently difficult to control (e.g. soldering Printed Circuit Boards). Improved process controls and "burn in screening" are common corrective actions.

- When Weibull behavior indicates constant hazard rate (i.e. $\beta=1$), the tendency to fail is independent of accumulated usage, with new units being neither better nor worse than old units. For this failure regime, age replacement of units has little effect but increased maintenance costs. The remediation strategy when $\beta=1$ is derating, redundancy or redesign for robust failure locations.

- When Weibull behavior indicates wear-out failure (i.e. $\beta>1$), early life failures are rare, but increase with service hours. Depending on replacement cost and consequence, wear-out failure is appropriately addressed by maintenance, replacement on a service hour determined schedule or feature redesign. Unacceptably short wear-out performance of safety critical equipment is best addressed by feature redesign.

Large Beta & Eta Values:

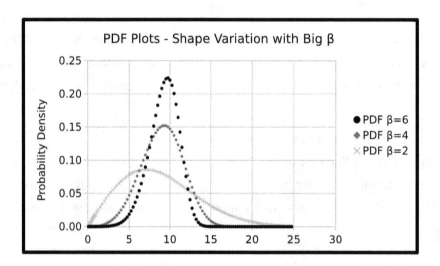

Figure 6-9: Effect of Larger Beta Values

Moderate Beta values (1.5 to 2.5) describing equipment failure indicate few early failures, but once sufficient usage has accumulated, failures will begin and increase in frequency. High Beta Values (3.5 to 6) indicate very few early failures; but, once they start, large numbers of failures will decimate the product population in a short period of time.

Big Beta Values: A friend living on Guam owned a rental car fleet that included seven identical Asian imports. After three years of service, the driver's door handle "came apart" on one of these cars. Over the next five weeks, the remaining six driver door handles failed. Once failure began, all failed in a short period of time. The Beta value must have been large.

Big Eta Values: For equipment failure, eta (η) is the typical service life (measured in cycles, hours of operation, miles driven, number of landings or ...) parameter. Eta is the x value, by which 63.21% of the population will have failed (by the characterized mechanism). While people usually think in terms of averages, Eta is a measure somewhat beyond average.

In 2000, I began teaching English at a technical college in north Thailand. Like most of the teachers, I bought a 15 year old Honda Dream 100 as my means of transportation. After buying it, I replaced the main and rod bearings. I also replaced the drive chain and sprockets. For the next 2 years it rarely broke. It seems Honda engineers pushed η for nearly all wear-out mechanisms beyond 15 years of use – an incredible accomplishment.

Determining Probability from 2 Parameter Weibull Equations:

There are 2 equivalent interpretations of the area (from x=0 to x=a) under the PDF curve. As a matter of convenience, these will be explained in terms of a PDF describing equipment failure.

- The area under the PDF curve (from x=0 to x=a) represents the percentage of failed units from the population prior to usage time x=a. But the second interpretation below is perhaps more important.

- The area under the PDF curve (from x=0 to x=a) represents the probability that a particular/selected member of the population will fail prior to usage time x=a. That is to say, the PDF can rightfully be interpreted as the probability of failure of a particular item before some selected time.

While the probability statements above can be proved equivalent, it is far better for the reader to reflect on a bucket of "widgets" with some measured characteristic. The probability of a randomly picked "widget" having value less than "a" is the same as the percentage of population having measured value less than "a".

Once understood, it becomes clear that the PDF equivalently describes percentage of population but also probability of occurrence of a randomly picked sample.

Areas under the PDF curve thus have great importance; however, the PDF ALWAYS addresses the percentage of population (or probability) between x=0 and some value x=a to the right. The question thus arises, "How are we to deal with the area between points x=a and x=b?"

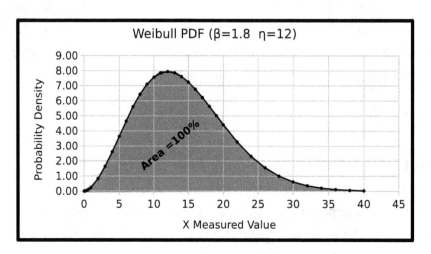

Figure 6-10: Total Area Under PDF Curve

We know that the total area under the probability curve is 100% because it represents the entire range of x measurements and all the members of a population. Taking the probability viewpoint, we could say "If you reach into the 'population bucket' and pull out a sample, it is 100% certain you will get a sample with some measured x value." While true, this statement is not very illuminating.

Far more illuminating are these questions:

- What percentage of (described) population has a value less than b?

- Taking the probability viewpoint: If you reach into the "population bucket" and pull out a widget, what is the probability the widget has an x measurement less than b?

118

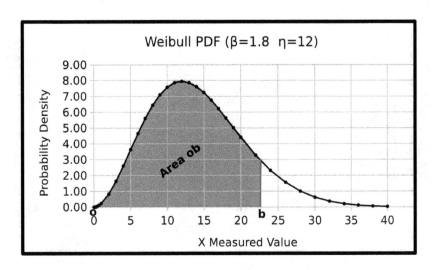

Figure 6-11: Finding PDF Area ob

Figure 6-11 shows the PDF graph and the area we wish to know; but, guessing at area is not accurate. The <u>CDF equation</u> corresponding to Figure 6-11 (see Eq 6-10) is <u>the efficient way</u> to determine area between origin (point o) and some point b shown on the Figure. Below, both the general form of the CDF and the result when β=1.8 and η= 12 are substituted are shown. Finally, we substitute 23 in lieu of x to compute gray area ob of Figure 6-11. (see Equation 6-10 below)

Eq 6-8 to 6-10

$$F(x) = 1 - e^{-\left(\frac{x}{\eta}\right)^{\beta}}$$

$$F(x) = 1 - e^{\left(-\left(\frac{x}{12}\right)^{1.8}\right)}$$

$$F(x) = 1 - e^{\left(-\left(\frac{23}{12}\right)^{1.8}\right)} = 96.03\%$$

Our final question is how to determine the population percentage (or associated "bucket probability") between two points x=a and x=b shown on Figure 6-12 following. Because the method is obvious, a single sentence will suffice.

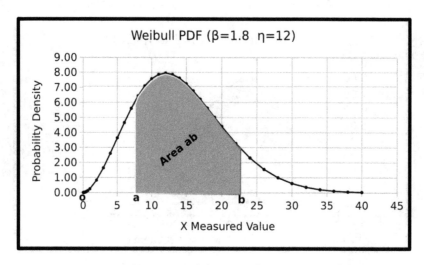

Figure 6-12: Finding Area between a and b

To find Area ab, we simply find areas ob, and oa separately, and subtract the smaller from the larger. i.e.

Eq 6-11: $\text{Area}_{ab} = \text{Area}_{ob} - \text{Area}_{oa}$

A Real World Example · Japanese Earthquakes

Severe earthquakes cause disproportionate damage. Policy makers want to know the percentage of earthquakes for the following Richter Scale ranges: 3-4, 4-5, 5-6, 6-7. Data from the Japan Meteorological Agency was analyzed to determine modeling parameters for the distribution.

- $\beta = 4.1956$ $\eta = 3.708$

The CDF Equation for Japanese January 2021 Earthquakes follows:

Eq 6-12

$$F(x) = 1 - \frac{1}{e^{\left(\left(\frac{x}{3.708}\right)^{4.1956}\right)}}$$

The forgoing equation, combined with Equation 6-11 enables percentage determination for various earthquake severity ranges as follows:

Magnitude 3-4=$[1-e^{(-4/3.708)^{4.1956}}]-[1-e^{(3/3.708)^{4.1956}}]$ =74.70%-33.71%=40.99%

Magnitude 4-5=$[1-e^{(-5/3.708)^{4.1956}}]-[1-e^{(-4/3.708)^{4.1956}}]$=97.00%- 74.70%=22.3%

Magnitude 5-6= similar =99.95% - 97.00%=2.95%

Magnitude 6-7= similar =100% - 99.95%= 0.05%

The prevalence of earthquakes of various magnitudes is summarized below.

2-3	33.71%
3-4	40.99%
4-5	22.23%
5-6	2.95%
6-7	0.05%

Table 6-1: Japanese Earthquake Severity

Computing Data-sample Median Values:

Optional: The reader will (hopefully) recall Chapter 3 stated that high probability data values occur at various locations along the x axis, and these are caused by more easily proven probability peaks (Median Percents) occurring in the PDF area. These observations naturally cause us to wonder how best we can identify preferred 1st, 2nd, 3rd, ... nth data-point peak x locations more formally called Median Values.

While this is of interest to individuals trying to justify statistical methods, it is rarely of practical concern when addressing "real world" problems. Despite rarity of practical use, it seems fair to show how this can be done. The method will be demonstrated by working an example and making use of the CDF equation.

Example: Given a data-set consisting of 4 points from a Weibull population with β=2 and η=24, determine the Median Values for each of the four data-points:

Step 1: Determine the Median Percents for each of 4 Median Values (use Benard's Equation)

Ordinal No	Median Percent
1	.1591
2	.3864
3	.6136
4	.8409

Table 6-2: Median Percents

Step 2: Begin with CDF Equation 4-4. Isolate x on left side, move all else to right side:

Eq 6-13

$$F(x) = 1 - \frac{1}{e^{\left(\frac{x}{\eta}\right)^{\beta}}} \rightarrow x = \eta \cdot \left[- \ln(1 - F(x)) \right]^{\left(\frac{1}{\beta}\right)}$$

Step 3: Create particular equation using known parameters β and η.

Eq 6-14

$$x = 24 \cdot [- \ln(1 - F(x))]^{\left(\frac{1}{2}\right)}$$

Step 4: F(x) in Eq 6-14 is cumulative percentage (such as .1591). Proceed by substituting the 1st Median Percent from table above into the equation, and solve for x using a scientific calculator. The value determined is the Median Value corresponding the 1st Median Percent for the data-set.

Eq 6-15

$$x = 24 \cdot [- \ln(1 - .1591)]^{\left(\frac{1}{2}\right)} = 9.99$$

Table 6-3

Ordinal Number	Median Prcnt	Median Value
1	.1591	9.99
2	.3864	16.77
3	.6136	23.40
4	.8409	32.54

Repeat the process for remaining 3 data-points.

122

Chapter 6 Summary:

Equations and their behavior for both the 3 parameter Weibull and the 2 parameter Weibull were presented in Chapter 6. The focus of Chapter 6 is on the equation forms and the effect of parameters β, η and Xo.

For the 3 Parameter Weibull: Two general equation forms are presented (1st for PDF, and 2nd for CDF). These equations are written in terms of parameters β, η and Xo. The effect of each parameter is illustrated in Figures 6-1 and 6-9.

- 3 Parameter Weibull: The x domain is from x equals Xo to infinity. Xo is the x axis starting point for the distribution. Parameter η establishes x location "trapping" 63% of population (slightly greater than the mean). β value determines PDF curve shape.

- The 2 parameter Weibull equations (PDF and CDF) are special cases of the 3 parameter equations where Xo equals zero, thus establishing the PDF x axis starting point at x=0. Parameters η and β have the same effect as for the 3 parameter distribution.

The Weibull Plot is based on a transformed set of x values, and corresponding transformed Median Percents for each data point. For a population with domain truly beginning at x=0, the Weibull Plot clearly establishes parameters β and η ; however, the analyst has no means of knowing beyond doubt that the population truly begins at x=0.

- If the x domain begins at zero, determination of β and η parameters by Weibull Plot is a "closed form solution" leading directly to answers. When Weibull Plot methods are applied to a population beginning at Xo different from zero, a trial and error approach is needed to identify the Xo starting point of the distribution.

- When an arced set of data-points "surrounds" the Weibull Plot fit line, it is strong indication that a 3 parameter analysis is needed to describe the population. In such circumstance, "data arc" must be addressed regardless of R^2 value.

- Routine analysis and comparison of results by both 2 and 3 parameter methods is recommended whenever technical means are available because data-scatter unfortunately obscures observation of "curved arc data" about the Weibull Plot.

When plotting PDF and CDF equations, the computed y values can be quite small leading one to believe something is wrong with spreadsheet equations. Often, the equations are correct, but the analyst is examining the wrong range of values. For a two parameter Weibull, it is usually appropriate to graph values of x between 0.01 and two times η. About 20 to 25 values in that range usually produces a reasonable plot. Usually it is helpful to use small x increments for the first dozen data-points. Also, graphing x=0 will likely cause an error message as does graphing a 3 parameter PDF for x<Xo)

For equipment failures, the Beta parameter describing a population indicates what failure behavior should be expected for the analyzed failure mode/s.

- β<1 indicates early failures, with older in service units performing with fewer problems than younger units.

- β=1 indicates that failure tendency from the analyzed mechanism of failure is independent of time in service.

- β >1 indicates a wear-out mode of failure. This means newer units will tend to work well, but as equipment accumulates service time, failures will begin and become more common.

There exist prescribed ways of addressing each of the Beta regimes as discussed in the preceding chapter. While the generalizations above apply universally, the prescribed means of addressing the three regimes is only effective when Weibull Analysis is applied to single modes of failure.

Chapter Footnotes:

1. From the Warwick Group. Article titled The Use of Weibull in Defect Data Analysis, https://warwick.ac.uk/fac/sci/wmg/ftmsc/modules/modulelist/rdd/temp/weibull.pdf Revision Date 6 December 2004. Article offers a broad discussion of Weibull and provides in depth comments regarding the interpretation of Weibull failures based on various values of the shape coefficient β.

Homework Chapter 6:

Homework Hints for Plotting PDF and CDF based on known β and η:

- Use a spreadsheet and set up column A to represent a range of x values. Space out about 20 values over the desired x range. X should begin with .01 or .03 and not from zero. The full range of values should stretch out to about 2 or 3 times η.

- Use an equation (6-3 or 6-4) to compute the Y value. Use either PDF or CDF equation according to the graph that you want.

- You will need to use an X-Y graph option in your spreadsheet.

- Add Graph titles according to your desire (Your name might be a nice sub-title.)

- Spreadsheet entry of the equations tends to be rather fussy. If you have trouble getting it right for the PDF, break the calculations into 3 columns (col B, C, D), and then multiply them together in column E. If you take this approach, you will have to copy x values into column F and your Y computed values into column G. Then plot off Columns F and G.

Figure 6-8 will give a good idea of what your PDF should look like.

Figure 6-7 will give a good idea of what your CDF should look like.

1. For $\beta = 2.5$ and $\eta = 10$, use a spreadsheet to plot the 2 parameter Weibull for the following:

- The PDF from x=0 to x=25

- The CDF from x=0 to x=25

2. For $\beta = 1$ and $\eta = 15$, use a spreadsheet to plot the 2 parameter Weibull for the following:

- The PDF from x=0 to x=30

- The CDF from x=0 to x=30.

3. Begin with the general Weibull CDF Equation 6-4. Perform algebra to isolate x on the left and all other variables and parameters on the right side of "equals". Hint: please remember that $\ln(e^x) = x$

4. Use steps below to calculate Median Value for each of 4 experimental data-points:

- Calculate Median Percent for each data-point (Benard Eq else Linear Conjecture)

- Use a Weibull Plot with X-Y trend-line and equation to determine β and η

- Perform algebraic manipulation of CDF equation 6-4 to isolate x variable on left.

- Use the result above to determine Median Value for each of 4 points below

	Measured x	Median Value
1	10.41	
2	17.07	
3	23.95	
4	35.20	

5. Review Question: if β=3.8 and η=50.5, compute the Median Percents for a data-set of 5 points. Use the Linear Conjecture method from Chapter 3.

6. Review Question: If β=3.8 and η=50.5, determine median percents for each ordinal location (1,2,3,4,5) for a data-set of five points.

7. If data analysis indicates β=1.5 and η=30.3, write the CDF equation describing probabilities for the data-set (i.e. write the particular CDF equation describing the data-set).

8. In ¼ page or less, explain why the PDF always results in a percent number where-as in real life things either happen, or don't happen. In real life, during 2021 Japan may experience 3 or perhaps 4 severe earthquakes, whereas our mathematics will indicate something like 3.28 severe earthquakes? Why to you think the statistical approach is necessary?

9. Thought Question: Recall that Chapter 2 stated "The population viewpoint is that the population is frozen in time and the data-set merely represents that population …. Even in situations where some of the data has not yet been recorded we assume the population is frozen in time…. If WWI doctors measured several small feet during a week they would not conclude 'this week, feet are shrinking daily."

Do you believe that a bucket containing 96 black marbles and 4 red ones will most likely result in a 'black marble grab'? Do you think the "frozen in time" viewpoint justifies predictions based on population characterization? Why do you think that? Can you explain in half a page or less?

Chapter 7: Weibull Analysis - What Can Go Wrong?

Chapter Goals:

Chapter 7 is a survey of the kinds of issues that can cause Weibull Analysis to misrepresent a population. Six classes of issues are identified and resolutions discussed.

1. Attempted Weibull Analysis of deterministic or deterministic/stochastic data-sets.

2. Weibull Plots with too few data-points.

3. Use of 2 parameter Weibull analysis when 3 parameter analysis is needed.

4. Analysis of commingled mechanism data-sets.

5. Insistent use of Weibull Analysis on non-Weibull populations.

6. Weibull Plots with R^2 < 90%.

Attempted Weibull Analysis of Deterministic Data-sets:

Misapplication of Weibull Analysis to a deterministic data-set was discussed in Chapter 2. Processes are deterministic, stochastic or some mix of the two, thus resulting in data-sets of like type. A deterministic process is a series of events, each of who's outcomes is certain. Deterministic processes result in a sequence of predictable states yielding a preordained outcome. Statistical analyses are generally ineffective at describing deterministic outcomes.

A mixed process has both random and deterministic influences. Weibull analysis is likely to be effective when such processes exhibit very gradual change as illustrated by Figure 7-1

As a common sense criteria, <u>Weibull analysis of raw data should not be used when data trend line total rise is more than 15% of the overall y axis data scatter</u>. In such circumstance, trend

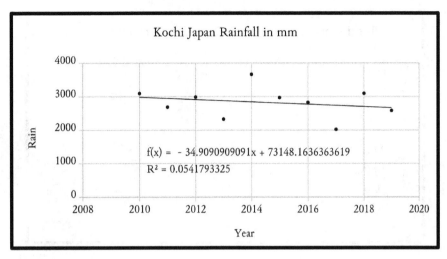

Figure 7-1: Kochi Japan Rain-fall Trend

induced errors become significant relative to typical Beta inference errors.

When trending is dominant, a purely Weibull Analysis should not be used. In such circumstance, either a physics based description or an ad hoc trend-line analysis like the one below should be used to describe the data.

Perhaps the best method to determine whether a data-set is predominately deterministic is to create multiple x-y plots. Each x-y plot examines how "x variable of interest" changes in response to some other variable. Trend line plot Figure 7-2 indicates equatorial location has greater effect on temperature than random variation thus modeling should be deterministic (not statistical).

Example: A survey was taken of 40 cities world wide. Data included average temperature, latitude and altitude. Figure 7-2 was prepared to determine whether latitude is a dominant determiner of mean annual temperature. The figure shows a trend line drop of 60C from left to right with a typical data scatter band of 10C about the fitted line. Latitude thus seems to have strong influence over temperature and random scatter is secondary. To produce Figure 7-2, the data was sorted by latitude, to enable identification of temperature dependence on latitude. The figure confirms expectation that cities farther north are colder.

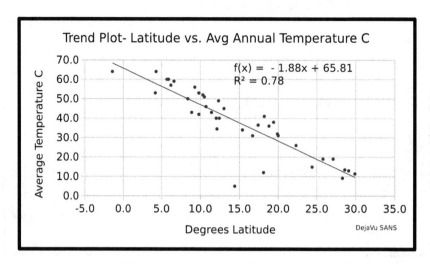

Figure 7-2: Temperature Dependence on Latitude

From a statistical perspective, we want to know whether a data set is stochastic (driven by random processes), or whether it is deterministic. In the former case, statistical analysis such as Weibull is appropriate. If the data is deterministic, Weibull or other statistical analysis methods are not recommended and either physics based methods or ad hoc curve correlations (as shown above) likely provide far better characterizations.

The purpose of analysis is to provide accurate characterization of data that can advance the interests of engineering, science or business. Confronted with evidence of the overwhelming effect of latitude, why would we try to characterize temperature as random while ignoring a known and dominant influence? Rather than clinging to an incorrect analysis approach, we must often use alternative methods including deterministic relationships. A typical summary report for Figure 7-2 follows.

"It was determined that mean annual temperature based on a survey of 40 world wide locations is best described by an ad hoc linear relationship based on equatorial distance (i.e. degrees latitude). The moderately strong trend correlation identified by the figure is far more accurate than a statistical description of average annual temperature."

Eq 7-1:   Mean Annual Temperature = -1.88*latitude + 65.81   with R^2 = 78%

Considerable scatter is evident for 2 data-points. Review of possible dependencies (such as altitude) is recommended to address this unexplained anomaly. If these two data-points were adequately addressed, the resulting curve fit would approach $R^2 = 98\%$."

Weibull Plots with too few data-points.

Perhaps the most powerful way to convince readers of small data-set inaccuracy is to provide results from a four times repeated "real life" experiment. Interested readers should turn to Appendix J which reports on results of selecting five random samples from a population of 16 before estimating population parameters. The four estimates vary greatly, accurately describing the population about half the time. Results improve greatly with larger data-sets.

There is disagreement regarding how many data-points are needed to perform a dependable Weibull Analysis with some experts claiming a strength of Weibull Analysis is its ability to produce conclusions based on small data-sets. While Weibull Analysis sometimes produces such results, extreme caution is advised.

A group of engineers was asked how accurately they could define a straight line equation through two data-points, and the group replied, "Accurate to 10 decimal places of my calculator." A confidence analysis would have concurred; but I don't.

Issue 1: Does the "fitted line" correlate tightly to the data-points? This is normally quantified by R^2 values at the fitted line level of detail with 99.9% indicating excellence. But with only two data points for a straight line, it is like having only two people vote for mayor. There is little opportunity for dissent and R^2 becomes meaningless.

Issue 2: There exist "confidence bounds" that can be provided above and below the Weibull line drawn through a set of data-points (see Figure 7-3). Confidence bounds are based on data point consistency; but, there is always a "dumb luck chance" that five data points in a row may conform to a Weibull; yet are offset or tilted. Confidence bounds cannot detect such circumstance if the data points are otherwise well behaved.

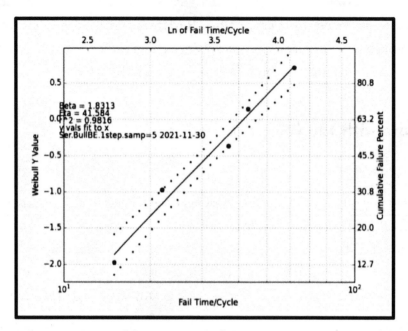

Figure 7-3: Confidence Bounds (Watson Weibull Program)

Most Weibull Analysis software is capable of creating Confidence Bounds. The "slightly curved" dotted lines above and below the "best fit" Weibull line are 90% Confidence Bounds. It is generally accepted in industry that if the five point experiment were repeated many times, 90% of repeat analyses would generate "best fit" lines trapped between the upper and lower dotted lines. Phrased a bit differently, I might say there is 90% confidence that the bounds provided trap the true position of the Weibull line. With this understanding, it is clear that 99% confidence bounds will be more widely spread about the fit line than 90% confidence bounds. It is significant that the repeat experiments discussed above would likely result in data-points outside the illustrated upper and lower boundaries and there exist similar methods for bounding these. Confidence bounds address expected Weibull Line position – not data-point scatter.

When applying confidence bounds during analysis, the analyst must decide the Percent Confidence level desired. For safety critical circumstance, 99% confidence is usual. Individuals interested in how confidence bounds are calculated should consult Dr. Charles Zaiontz's www.Real-Statistics.com web site.

My attempts to provide a practical answer for the required number of points have not yet been conclusive. For now, the best advice is:

- Get as many data-points as possible - preferably more than 19 and never less than 5.

- Use Statistical Confidence Bounds to get an idea of the variability of β, η implied by data scatter about "fitted Weibull line".

2 Parameter Weibull When 3 Parameter Weibull is Required:

A population, has items that are not arranged according to human convenience. They simply are as they are. A population is most intuitively described by a histogram showing the quantity of various "x measured value buckets" in the population.

Figure 7-4 below shows two histograms representing two different populations. At the left is a population who's smallest members begin at an x value very near 0. At the right, is a population of items who's members members begin at an x value of 10.

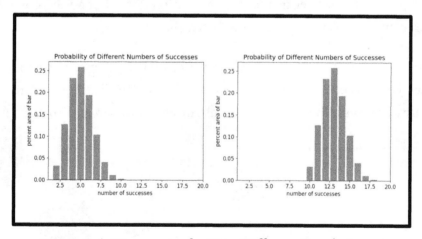

Figure 7-4: Histograms for Two Different Populations

The 2 parameter Weibull is incapable of adequate modeling of Figure 7-4 right since the 2 parameter Weibull PDFs <u>always</u> begins at x=0. When the analyst incorrectly forces 2 parameter modeling onto the right illustration, terrible distortions of the PDF shape occur. In particular, the left corner point x=10 is stretched over to the origin. The resultant increase in width attempts to increase the total area which must remain 100%. To address the area problem, the math forces an extremely narrow peaked PDF and thus a very large β.

It is not of great benefit to describe the acrobatics performed by math as it tries to force a 2 parameter Weibull onto a data population with an initial Xo offset. The important things to realize are:

- A 3 parameter Weibull equation can describe the "offset" right image of Figure 7-4. Chapter 10 presents a detailed discussion of the 3 parameter Weibull.

- The population being analyzed is inherently one of the following: 2 parameter Weibull, 3 parameter Weibull or something else. It must be analyzed for what it is in the same way that a mechanic must match his wrench to whatever size a bolt is.

- Observation of "arced data" (See Figure 7-5) on a 2 parameter Weibull Plot is the only observable evidence that a 3 parameter Weibull was incorrectly analyzed as 2 parameter. Unfortunately, data scatter makes this observation difficult, and there are several other data problems that can also cause this "arced shape".

- A spreadsheet is not an effective tool for performing 3 parameter analysis. Commercial software is more accurate and far more cost effective. While not recommended, alternatives to commercial software are discussed below, along with examples of "arced data".

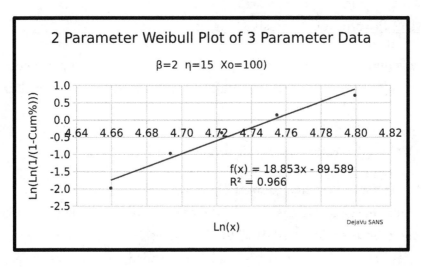

Figure 7-5: Arced Data without Data Scatter

Figure 7-5 depicts 3 parameter Weibull data that has been incorrectly analyzed by 2 parameter methods. It can be observed from Figure 7-5 that even a slight arc of data about the Weibull Plot line indicates need for a 3 parameter Weibull analysis. The sub-header identifies the true Weibull parameter values, which are greatly different from those indicated by the inappropriately applied 2 parameter Weibull Plot above.

A Spreadsheet Approach:

If a spreadsheet is constructed with an extra column that allows reducing data-point x values by amount Xo (usually assigned as a variable at top of column) enabling Pseudo X as Ln(x-Xo), then a correct Weibull Plot without "data-point arc" can be identified. When spreadsheet methods are applied to 3 parameter analysis, the analyst usually creates the Weibull Plot before substituting various guesses of Xo. Most spreadsheets will respond dynamically with the graph, allowing the analyst to observe data-points about the line and R^2. When true straight line data-points occur and R^2 is maximized, the attempted Xo is correct. This method is difficult because data scatter obscures data arc, and many guesses of Xo are needed before the optimum value is found.

<u>3 Parameter vs. 2 Parameter Analysis Conclusion:</u>

The central issue is human inability to identify a data-set as either 2 or 3 parameter Weibull. Even after performing a 2 parameter Weibull Plot, the matter often remains unclear.

- When commercial software is readily accessible, routine performance and comparison of 2 parameter vs. 3 parameter analysis is recommended.

- When the analyst is restricted to spreadsheet analysis, the 3 parameter solution is awkward and undependable. As a result, the analyst will likely rely on 2 parameter analysis and evaluation of "arced data" to identify cases where 3 parameter analysis is absolutely essential. This approach is not recommended, but analysts in some companies may not be supported when Weibull Software purchase is requested.

Analysis of Commingled Failure Mechanism Data-sets.

A commingled data-set refers to data belonging to equipment (or test items) that represents a variety of failure mechanisms grouped together. Data-points are simply identified as failures. Commingled data-sets can be collected for either "throw away" equipment, or equipment which is repaired when needed. For repairable equipment, it is obviously possible for a variety of failure types to manifest and be grouped together as a data-set.

Non-repairable (i.e. throw-away) equipment is plagued by the question "Can commingling really happen?" For example, consider a computer hard drive that exhibits two failure modes, each describable by a Weibull distribution, but having very different Eta parameters. While a composite Weibull Plot can easily be created, there are credibility issues. If the disk drive becomes non-serviceable after either failure mode, we should expect the the failure mode having the smaller eta to remove all drives from service before 2nd mode failures are encountered. Hence, all or most drives would be removed from failure by the 1st mode and very few (if any) by the 2nd mode.

Yet, there are situations where mixed mode failure may be observed. Consider a "throw away" computer hard drive that includes critical capacitors bought from two different factories. It is possible that drives equipped with Capacitor A fail early, but those with Capacitor B will not. This would allow half the drives with "weak capacitors" to fail, while the other half would remain serviceable until predated by the 2nd failure mode.

Except for special purposes, I do not recommend mixed failure mode data-set analysis; however, the concept is possible and three examples of the effect of multi-mode data-sets on Weibull Plots are provided. The examples show that multi-mode analysis can cause a variety of mal formed Weibull Plots, some of which appear to be "arced data-sets" thus falsely signaling a need for 3 parameter analysis.

Commingled Data-sets: The Classic Crooked Weibull Plot:

When β values are significantly different (1.5 vs. 5.5), commingling of 2 data-sets creates an abrupt "crook" in the slope traced by data-points as shown by Figure 7-6. The relationship of the η values determines whether the transition is abrupt as shown below.

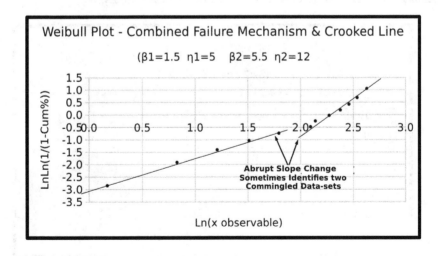

Figure 7-6: An Abrupt Crook from Commingled Data

Commingled Data-sets: 2 Slopes with Smoother Transition:

The Weibull Plot below has the same β values as before, but η values are closer together. A "smoother" transition results and "arced data" falsely suggests 3 parameter analysis.

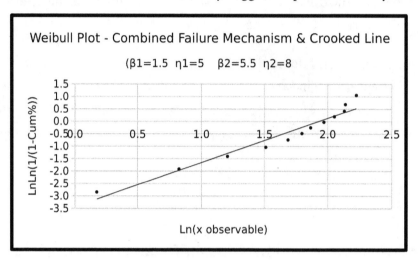

Figure 7-7: Combined Failure Mode Data

Commingled Data-sets: Three Fail Modes with Different η :

The last example mixes three data-sets, all with $\beta=2$. Different η values result in "arced data" which again falsely indicates the need for 3 parameter Weibull analysis.

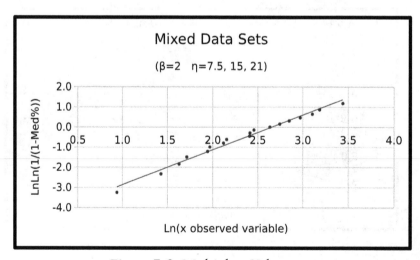

Figure 7-8: Multiple η Values

Commingled Data-set Effect on PDF:

We have viewed examples showing how commingled data affects Weibull Plots; but, now we consider commingling effects on the PDF. For this discussion, we once again assume that Weibull is used to describe failure behavior of a machine or product.

First, we consider the truth or falsity of the belief that multiple PDFs each describing its own failure mode can meaningfully be combined into a single PDF. The answer to this question determines whether (or not) multiple well understood failure models can be combined to represent the overall life performance of a machine.

In most cases, experience can be used as a guide to ensure that each considered failure mode is independent. Returning to the automotive example, it is clear that water pump failure is unaffected by wear-out of the brake system. In such a case, separate Weibull Distributions independently represent failure behavior for each failure mode. If we simple add the y values of the two separate Weibull PDFs, the composite PDF indicates 200% failure. We must therefor divide the composite CDF height by 2 to retain 100% area under the PDF. This example is a simplification of the real situation (it assumes 1 failure of each type during the life of a car). This basic approach was used to create Figure 7-9 below.

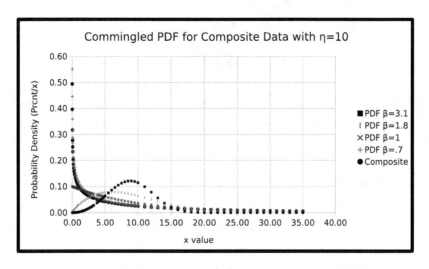

Figure 7-9: Commingled Data Composite PDF

The composite Weibull PDF representing four separate failure modes (each with its own unique Weibull PDF) is shown by the round black data-points of Figure 7-9. Also represented are the four different contributing Weibulls with βs between .7 and 3.

As frequently happens with commingled data-sets, the composite Weibull PDF has a β of .688 thus looks like a decreasing exponential failure distribution. The commingled η value at 12.91 is fairly close to the η of contributing failure modes. The composite PDF likely describes overall failure behavior; but, insight gained from individual failure PDFs has been lost.

The reader will recall that distinct failure mode Weibulls result in βs that give hints regarding needed corrective action. β= .7 suggests a likelihood of poor quality control during assembly while β=3 suggests a need for either design changes or alternatively an effective maintenance program.

We conclude that commingled failure mode analysis likely describes long term machine behavior; but, it does not provide insight into fundamental product problems.

Commingled Data Conclusions:

For Weibull Plots, commingled data from multiple failure modes creates a number of erroneous geometries and false interpretations including:

- "Arced Data" false indication of need for 3 parameter Weibull analysis.

- Sharp or curved transitions between 2 separate data-point slopes.

- A variety of other malformed Weibull Plot geometries.

For Weibull PDFs, commingled data from multiple failure modes is likely to replace multiple β values with a single β less than 1 (thus some form of decreasing exponential). While overall life failure behavior is likely described by the composite Weibull PDF, useful β inference of failure cause and corrective action is lost. Unless intended for a specific and understood purpose, Weibull analysis of commingled data-sets is not recommended.

Insistent Use of Weibull Analysis on a Nonconforming Data-set:

The Weibull distribution has an amazing ability to adapt its shape to various data-sets; but, adaptability does have limits. The following example shows what happens when Weibull is insistently misapplied. A notional triangular PDF distribution was created and its values calculated for a data-set. The data-set was then analyzed by Weibull methods resulting in β and η of 2.73 and 7.7 respectively. The triangular PDF was then superimposed on the Weibull PDF. Below, we see the consequences. Weibull predicts values to x=14; but the actual distribution has no values beyond 10.

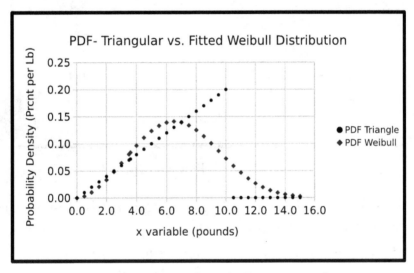

Figure 7-10: Imposition of Weibull on Triangular PDF

Previously, Figure 7-9 illustrated the result when a Weibull Plot is used to infer a 2 parameter Weibull PDF from a commingled data-set consisting of four failure modes having various β values. While Figure 7-9 is accurate as described, it is interesting that summing the various failure information from the four failure mode plots actually results in an odd looking PDF, which is not exactly Weibull. The analyst must decide if it is good enough.

In my judgment, if R^2 of the Weibull Plot is greater than 93%, it is good enough. If less than 90%, it definitely is not good enough. R^2 between these two values requires judgment. Arced data is an exception and often produces very poor results regardless of R^2.

Weibull Plots with R^2 Values < 90%

Weibull plots with R^2<90% should not be used to infer underlying populations. The Weibull line below does not correlate well to the data because the data is poor.

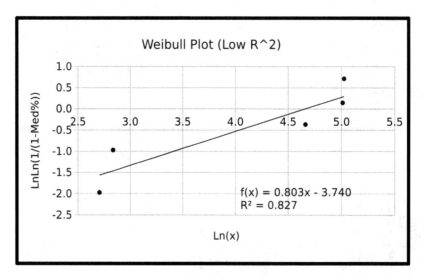

Figure 7-11: Weibull Plot with Low R^2

In daily life, 83% will earn a solid B in any college course, so we falsely assume that R^2 = 83% must be acceptable; but, this belief is wrong. R^2 is computed percent reduction in sum of squared distance from mean y value, that results from using the fitted line, i.e.

Eq 7-2   R^2= Σ(Yi of fitted line – Yavg)^2 / Σ(Yi – Yavg)^2 (see Schaums p243)

While this approach is usual for statisticians, it is a feeble standard. When a data-set conforms closely to a fitted equation, R^2 values are typically greater than 98%. Reliance on Weibull Plots with R^2 < 90% is not recommended. Values of R^2 less than 85% are often associated with wildly wrong β and η. The above plot with R^2=83% looks bad and it is bad.

Chapter 7 Addendum: What is a Single Failure Mode?

A Weibull analysis is ideally performed on data representing a single failure mode or mechanism. The term "single mode" is intended to be quite specific as shown by the following examples.

- Test of Rivet Shear Strength: Shear of the rivet is regarded as a different mode of failure than popping the head off a rivet. Pulling the rivet head through joined metal plates is yet a different failure mode. If failure by shear is the intent of a test, then failure by the other two modes is "discard data" (called "suspended data" in many other books.)

- Analysis of automotive break wear-out: Wear-through of the friction surface is regarded as a different mode of failure from leakage of the break hydraulic pistons. For disk brakes, warping of the rotor is yet a different failure mode. During analysis of friction material wear-out, these other two failure modes are "discard data."

- Printed Circuit Board Failure: For printed circuit board failure analysis, data from PCB replacement caused by capacitor failure should not be combined with data from solder joint cracking. These are distinct failure modes. Arguably, surface mount component solder joints should be treated as distinct (surface shear), from through hole solder joint cracking because of the very different geometry and crack path.

- For San Francisco earthquake analysis, quake data from the San Andreas is likely a different failure mechanism than quake data from other fault lines in the area. Sometimes, the "rip length" of earthquakes is known raising further questions. When sufficient data is available, the analyst should evaluate the data in various ways to try and isolate the various component data-sets. In practice, data quantity and quality is often not sufficient and the analyst is forced to do the best he/she can with data available.

In engineering, the restrictive use of Weibull to single failure modes is problematic because it is often difficult to justify diagnosis of failed part returns. Often, identification of the failure mode is difficult. As a result, many companies believe field return evaluation is only justified for safety related failures.

Chapter 7 Summary: Six classes of Weibull misapplication have been identified and graphic examples provided:

- Weibull Analysis should not be used for deterministic data-sets.

- A sufficient number of data-points is required. 20+ is recommended; but never less than 5. There is no industry agreed minimum number but 5 is bad, 20 usually produces reasonable results and 35 is far better.

- Some populations demand use of a 3 parameter Weibull. Because there is always uncertainty, it is best to run both analyses and compare the results.

- Commingling of data from multiple event mechanisms should be avoided unless performed for very specific and understood reasons.

- Avoid insistent use of a Weibull PDF when it clearly does not describe the population. Fit of Weibull to population is best determined by Weibull Plot.

- Weibull Plots with R^2 less than 90% should not be used as they produce erratic results. R^2 values greater than 93% usually yield good results. The best available method for judging Weibull results is use of Confidence Bounds; but, even this is insufficient.

Chapter 7 Homework:

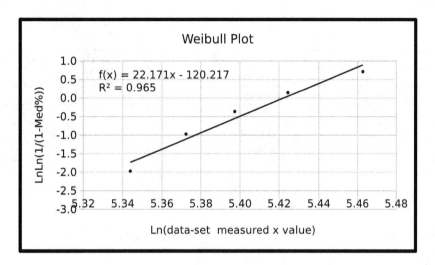

1. Based on the Weibull Plot above, document your best surmise of what is wrong with the Weibull Analysis or data-set. Document your conclusions in less than a quarter page.

2. Based on the Weibull Plot below, what do you think is wrong with the data-set or analysis?

- Identify and describe any plot abnormalities in less than a quarter page.

- What should be done to correct the analysis?

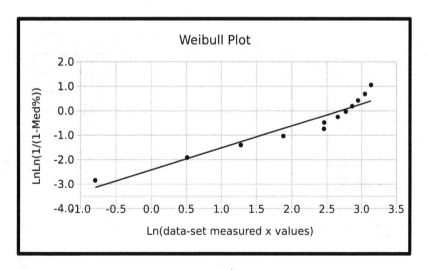

3. The fighting distance between battleships was recorded over a 50 year period with the following result:

Date	Conflict	Battle Distance
1898	Spanish-American War	2000 yds
1904	Russo-Japanese War	7000 yds
1916	WW1 - Jutland	16000 yds
1939	Hood v Bismarck	20000 yds
1943	WWII- Guadalcanal	16000 yds

Is it appropriate to perform a Weibull Analysis on this data?

- Why yes, or why no? Explain in less than a quarter page.

- If no, what alternative would you suggest to describe this data?

4. In 1587, Alfonso deLeon dropped a rock from the great tower in Pizza Italy. Assistants with water clocks stationed on identified floors recorded the elapsed time from release as the rock "whizzed past their feet." The data from observers is presented in the table below.

Floor	Fall Dist (feet)	Seconds
7	.01	.1
5	20	1.12
3	40	1.58
1	60	1.77

- Aside from the preposterous nature of the story, can Weibull Analysis be reasonably performed on this data? Why or why not?

- Should an x-y trend analysis be performed on this data? Why or why not?

5. Tsunami Wave Analysis: The historical height of 38 tsunamis was extracted from multiple Internet sources. The records include great waves between 1605 and 2020. Most recorded heights were at villages where the great waves struck. Despite data deficiencies, a Weibull Analysis was performed with the following result.

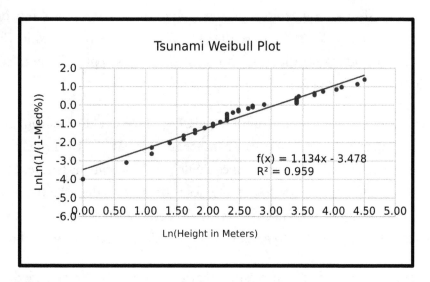

- Does the Weibull Plot above exhibit anomalies that concern you? If yes, what are the questionable aspects? Document in less than ¼ page.

- By reverse calculation, compute the approximate height in meters of the tallest wave.

- I created a Tsunami PDF plot below. You are asked to use a spreadsheet to create the CDF plot. Add your name in the title of the plot. Note: See Appendix H Equations.

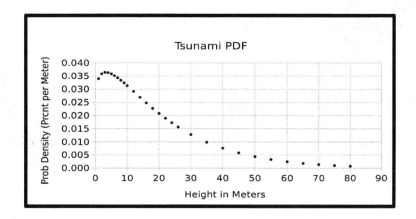

147

Chapter 8: Weibull Risk Analysis, Present & Future:

Risk analysis makes predictions!

A Weibull Risk Analysis based on geologic history, can determine the probability of a major Washington/Oregon earthquake in the next 10 years. The methods presented in Chapter 8 are sufficient to make this and many other predictions. Risk analysis applies to flu infections, tsunamis, equipment failure and rental fleet maintenance.

The PDF and CDF are believed to describe a population which could be earthquake severity, tsunami height, equipment failure intervals, shark length, etc.. While the principles below are broadly applicable, much of Chapter 8 examines single mode equipment failure. In this context, a Weibull PDF and CDF with known β and η values is believed to describe the probability of equipment failure based on an x variable (which might represent years of service or operational hours or number of landings, miles driven, or even intervals between major earthquakes.)

In the context of Risk Analysis, it is interesting that probabilities are often added together, and in some strange way, the sum is construed as "a number of events." For example, during battleship combat, if there is a 40% chance of hitting on the first salvo, and a 60% chance on the 2nd and 80% chance on the third, it is often assumed that the number of hits from 3 salvos is 40%+60%+80%=1.8 hits on the enemy. It seems to me that hits by a cannon are much like bananas. They should be counted 1, 2, 3... and I have trouble visualizing 1.8 hits from a cannon. This "adding of probabilities" conflates probability with actual occurrence and fractional events is the unappealing consequence. Regardless of how we feel about this notion, it carries over into Risk Analysis and we will proceed accordingly.

Three Forms of Risk Analysis:

Weibull CDF values can be considered as either percentage of a population or probability of occurrence. The second viewpoint is taken when we discuss risk. There are three broad kinds of risk analysis, each explained below.

- Many problems involve a characterized Weibull population where the probability of various "x" values is described by the PDF and its related CDF. If the population is growing at a known rate, then the total number of events prior to any future time is easily computed. With both the total number and the percentage we care about known, the problem is easily solved. For example, the number of earthquakes after an identified "start time" is a growing population that proceeds at uniform rate because geologic time moves slowly (i.e. the number of earthquakes per day is fairly constant and historically recorded). Based on any assumed "start date," the number of earthquakes prior to any future time is easily computed. The Weibull distribution describes the percentage of concerning quakes, thus with both number and percent of concern known, we can easily compute the number of damaging quakes that will occur by some future date. These kinds of problems are solved using an unmodified CDF equation.

- Present Risk Analysis takes the viewpoint that the CDF can describe something of interest that began some time ago. For example: Perhaps a fleet of rent cars was bought several months ago. The manager may want to know the number of failures projected at time of purchase. Present Risk Analysis (based on an unmodified CDF) can determine the expected failures to date.

- Future Risk Analysis assumes some time "a" has occurred since the CDF was begun, and assesses the likelihood of events occurring between now (i.e. time="a") and some time "u" later. It is thus a forward looking assessment ending after some interval of future time. While Future Risk Assessment is usually based on time, it can be based on "time unrelated" variable "x" such as miles driven.

Example: General Risk Analysis for a Growing Population:

If you were responsible for establishing the building code for Japanese earthquake design, what Richter Scale earthquake level would you require buildings survive? Ideally, the criteria should be strict enough to render building collapse in the next 100 years unlikely.

Perform a General Risk Analysis to determine:

- The probability of Japan experiencing a major earthquake of magnitude 6.0 or greater per year.

- The probability of Japan experiencing a major earthquake of magnitude 9.0 or greater per year.

Based on the two calculations, state the criteria you would impose. Identify any further analyses you would perform before making a final recommendation.

A Weibull analysis of 226 earthquakes exceeding Richter magnitude 1.5 between January 27 and February 25, 2021 was performed to determine β and η describing Japanese earthquake severity. It was determined that β= 4.5714 and η= 3.959833 with R^2 =97.6% (see Figure 8-1 below for Weibull Plot establishing distribution of Japanese Earthquake Severity).

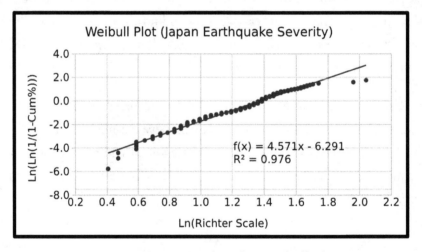

Figure 8-1: Japan Earthquake Weibull Plot

Step 1: Determine the average number of earthquakes per year:

226 events (magnitude 1.5 or greater) during 29 days implies 2846 earthquakes per year.

Step 2: Determine the percent of earthquakes having 6.0 magnitude or greater:

The general and particular form of the Weibull CDF follow, based on Weibull Plot 8-1.

Note: From Fig 8-1: β= 4.5714 and η= 3.959833

Eq 8-1

$$F(x) = 1 - \frac{1}{e^{\left(\left(\frac{x}{\eta}\right)^{\beta}\right)}}$$

Eq 8-2

$$F(x) = 1 - \frac{1}{e^{\left(\left(\frac{x}{3.96}\right)^{4.57}\right)}}$$

Evaluate the probability of any particular earthquake being below Richter Scale 6. i.e. x=6:

- Probability of Earthquake below 6: .998748 = 99.8748% (computed from Eq 8-2)

- Probability of Earthquake above 6:   1-.998748 = .001252 = .1252%

- Expected annual number: .001252 * 2846 quakes/year = 3.6

- Richter Scale 6 is insufficient. It would permit 3 or 4 damaging events per year.

Evaluate the probability of any particular earthquake being below Richter Scale 7.25

- Probability of quake below 7.25: $1 - 1.295668e-7$ = .99999 (from Eq 8-2)

- Probability of Earthquake above 7.25: 1 - (1 – 1.295668e-7) = 1.295668e-7

- Expected annual number: 2846 quakes x 1.295668e-7= .000369 quakes

- Expected years between such severe events = 1/.000369 = 2711 years between events

Conclusions:

- A building code requirement that structures withstand minimum of Richter Scale 6 earthquake is insufficient.

- A building code requirement that structures withstand minimum of Richter Scale 7.25 seems sufficient. The expected frequency of such events is approximately one in 2711 years.

Given potentially severe consequences, analysis refinement is needed. A data-set consisting of minimum 1 year of Japanese earthquake data should be analyzed to ensure the accuracy of β and η values. Available historical records of earthquake severity should also be reviewed. Note: In 2011, the Tohoku region experienced a Richter 9 quake. We are left wondering whether such an event was predictable.

The improved analysis should include 99% confidence bounds. Rather than using the "best fit" Weibull line (as above), the analysis should use a conservative "off-set" determined by the 99% confidence bounds to effectively lower the η value.

End point "data drupe" in Figure 8-1 indicates three parameter Weibull Analysis should be tried on the data to determine whether improved R^2 values result and to determine whether maximal "x" values are forced into conformance with the Weibull Plot line.

Implementation of the above three approaches should ensure performance of a conservative and defensible analysis. Given the safety risk to hundreds of thousands of people, these conservative measures are easily justified.

Present Risk Analysis:

Present risk analysis utilizes the Weibull CDF based on known β and η number values to compute the percentage of the population expected to have failed by the present time. When multiplied by "the number of items," it becomes a prediction of actual failed item count. As discussed previously, this prediction is likely to be a fractional number of failures such as 2.58 failures which can be construed as meaning two or three failures. In reality, a fleet manager already knows how many failures have occurred, thus Present Risk Analysis enables comparison of actual to expected failure counts.

Often, present risk analysis is performed on a fleet of many items. That fleet of objects (cars, motorcycles, helicopters, or drill presses) was likely purchased at various times and some of the items have been used more while others less. Because of this, the Present Risk equation is sometimes expressed as a summation, which indicates how each object is to be treated before adding up the results from individual items.

Performance of Present Risk Weibull Analysis requires knowledge of:

- The numeric values for β and η that describe failure behavior. (assumed as 2.5 and 15)

- The "service time" for each item at start of study. For example: "The landing gear actuation mechanism for a fleet of 3 type Q Helicopters had been exposed to the following landings: Copter 3 = 43. Copter 1 = 17. Copter 2 =19 landings.

- The Present Risk equation (Weibull CDF summed for each item.)

Eq 8-3
$$CDFPresentRisk = \Sigma_{i=1}^{N}\left[1 - \frac{1}{e^{\left(\frac{x_i}{\eta}\right)^{\beta}}} \right]$$

Eq 8-4
$$CDFPresentRisk = \Sigma_{i=1}^{N}\left[1 - \frac{1}{e^{\left(\frac{x_i}{15}\right)^{2.5}}} \right]$$

Eq 8-5
$$CDFPresentRisk = \left[1 - \frac{1}{e^{\left(\frac{17}{15}\right)^{2.5}}} \right] + ... + \left[1 - \frac{1}{e^{\left(\frac{43}{15}\right)^{2.5}}} \right]$$

Eq 8-6
CDF Present Risk=.7452+.8356+.9999=2.58

Step 3: Test based Weibull with β=2.5 and η=15 indicates two or three failures should have occurred. If field records are inconsistent with Risk Analysis results, it may be due to:

- Small data-set misidentification of β and η.

- Post qualification test redesign or process change.

- Difficulty of laboratory simulation of real environments.

Future Risk Analysis Without Replacement or Repair:

Future Risk Analysis is concerned with predicting the number of equipment failures (or events) most likely to occur by some future time. "Now time a" is selected relative to x=0 of the distribution (often based on actual service time of a sample). The elapse period until end of study is decided (i.e. How far in the future should the analysis project?). Finally, a modified Weibull CDF is used to compute the expected number of future events.

Future Risk Analysis without replacement or repair is usually not applied to expensive items like automobiles, excavators or concrete troweling machines. For inexpensive non-critical equipment such as bread toasters, this kind of analysis is appropriate. It is also appropriate for natural phenomena such as earthquakes, tsunami waves or levels of Japanese tea production.

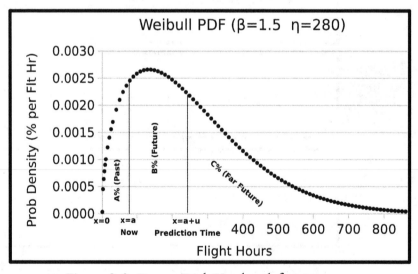

Figure 8-2: Future Risk X value definitions

Future Risk Analysis is concerned with what happens after "Now" defined by Figure 8-2 start time "a". Actual failures that may or may not have already occurred are not considered by the analysis. The analysis is performed to determine what is likely to happen with regard to units remaining in service when the study is initiated. When initiated, future time "a+u" is chosen which forms the end-point of the prediction interval. A modified Weibull CDF is the basis for item failure probability prediction. Finally, the sum of probabilities for the individual items becomes the predicted number of failures for a collection of items.

Optional: This kind of analysis applies equally to natural phenomena. For example, if a Weibull describes survival life of an endangered fish released into wildlife areas, and two releases are planned for the Lake Pontchartrain Louisiana, future risk without replacement/repair could be used to determine the expected survival number at some time "a+u" in the future. This would be done to ensure population overlap.

Referring to Figure 8-2, while the Weibull CDF will predict probability of failure for an item, the PDF starts with zero probability at time x=0. When summed over 0<x<infinity, the PDF correctly indicates 100% failures; but Future Risk is Different!

Future Risk Analysis begins at x="a" (study start time) and if extended to x=infinity should likewise indicate 100% failure of items in service at time "a". It is evident that some PDF area was consumed prior to time "a". Thus, the unmodified PDF from x="a" to infinity indicates failure of less than 100% of remaining items. The PDF needs adjustment to represent failure beginning at time "a". In essence, we must "vertically stretch" the PDF to force the PDF area right of x="a" to be 100%. The needed height factor is 1/[1-F(a)].

- a is the time when the Future Risk Prediction is started

- Using CDF: F(a) is the CDF prediction of area A% in Figure 8-2

The Future Risk modified CDF becomes: (1)

Eq 8-7
$$FutureRisk : F(x) = \frac{(F(a + u) - F(a))}{(1 - F(a))}$$

Note: The various terms [e.g. F(a)] are computed using Eq 8-1.

Application of the Future Risk Equation: There are two types of Future Risk problems.

- Future Risk Type 1, entails calculating the probability of a particular event occurring prior to some future x value 'a+u'. It is common to encounter Type 1 problems involving time.

- Future Risk Type 2, entails calculating how many of a particular event are likely to occur within a fleet of items having various ages. For example, given a fleet of 24 passenger jets with known accumulated usage hours, how many generator failures are expected in the next 5 years?

Type 1 problems: Using Equation 8-7 and 8-1:

Example Type 1 Future Risk Analysis : During WWII, US Navy aircraft-carrier planes had radial engines. Engine failure could be predicted using a Weibull Equation, with $\beta=1.5$ and $\eta=280$ flight hours (1)(2). These planes normally flew 2 hours to the target and 2 hours back. Engine failure CDF was expected to begin at take-off due to good maintenance.

If a Navy pilot flew to the target, dropped his bombs and started home, what is the probability he would return safely to his aircraft carrier without engine failure?

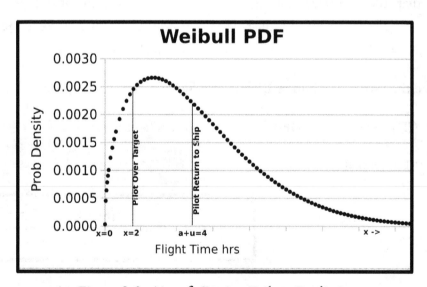

Figure 8-3: Aircraft Engine Failure Prediction

- Risk Analysis Start Time: a=2 hours (arrival over the target)

- Risk Study Endpoint Time (at ship return): i.e. a+u = 4 hours

- Use Eq 8-1 to compute F(a) and F(a+u) for use in equation 8-10:

Eq 8-8 for F(a)

$$F(x) = 1 - \frac{1}{e^{\left(\left(\frac{x}{\eta}\right)^{\beta}\right)}} = 1 - \frac{1}{e^{\left(\left(\frac{2}{280}\right)^{1.5}\right)}} = .0006 = .06\%$$

Eq 8-9 for F(a+u)

$$F(x) = 1 - \frac{1}{e^{\left(\left(\frac{x}{\eta}\right)^{\beta}\right)}} = 1 - \frac{1}{e^{\left(\left(\frac{4}{280}\right)^{1.5}\right)}} = .0017 = .17\%$$

Eq 8-10

$$FutureRisk: F(x) = \frac{(F(a+u) - F(a))}{(1 - F(a))} = > \frac{(.0017 - .0006)}{(1 - .006)} = .11\%$$

Prediction: The pilot had a 99.9% chance of returning to his ship without engine failure. The pilot had a .11% chance of falling into the ocean on his return trip.

Type 2 problems: Future Risk for Complex Fleet Distributions

Future Risk for a fleet having various "start conditions" is not fundamentally different from future risk analysis for a single item; except, that conditions at start time a, and at study end point a+u must be tracked by individual item. The euphemism "devil is in the details" could not be more true. This kind of problem is best addressed by spreadsheet. The equation that follows, is a modification of 8-7 that addresses the need to perform calculation separately for each item i, before adding up the results.

Future Risk applied to fleets of items requires Equations 8-11 and 8-12. As in the previous example, risk study is commenced at time "Now" which occurs at x="a". Many real world applications are concerned with a fleet of objects, each with a unique start time "ai" with respect to the CDF distribution (i.e. they have different ages when the risk study is initiated.) As an example, a fleet of 12 "identical" rent cars might have "Now" usage times as follows:

Col A	Col B	Col C	X "Now"
Car Number	In Service	Mile Range	Mile Midpoint
1,2	Jan 2021	4000-6000	5000
3	June 2020	6000-8000	7000
4,5,6	Feb 2020	8000-10000	9000
,8,9	July 2019	1000-12000	11000
10	Jan 2019	12000-14000	13000
11,12	May 2018	14000-16000	15000

Table 8-1: Fleet Mileage at Study Initiation

Because all cars are "identical" in the sense of being the same model, the probability of wear-out for each, is described by the same Weibull CDF; but, we have a problem. Accumulated service time when the study begins is different for the various cars:

- Cars 1 & 2, perceive time in service as 5000 miles (thus $a_{1,2}$ = 5000)

- Car 3, perceives time in service as 7000 miles (thus a_3 = 7000)

- Cars 4,5,6 perceive time in service as 9000 miles (thus a_{456} = 9000)

But each car also perceives a "forward looking" use time-span (e.g. $u_{1,2}$) prior to the desired Prediction Time. To address the various start and end points, each a,u pair must be uniquely identified, hence start-times are $a_1, a_2, ... a_N$ and similarly for end point times.

Figure 8-4 below depicts how cars 1, 2 and 3 see themselves in terms of the wear-out Weibull PDF. Both "start times a" and "prediction intervals u" are car specific.

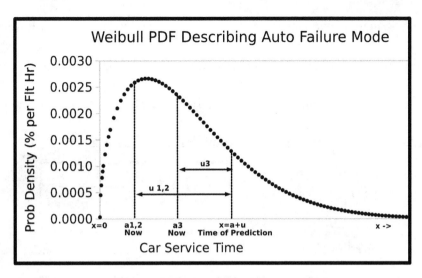

Figure 8-4: Auto Fleet Future Risk

To apply the Future Risk CDF to a fleet of items, Equation 8-7 must be modified to describe what is to be done for each item "i" (from item i=1 to N) for both start times ai and final times (ai+ui). The Future Risk CDF modified equation describing item i becomes:

Eq 8-11:
$$CDF:F(xi) = \frac{(F(ai - ui) - F(ai))}{(1 - F(ai))}$$

The predicted number of failures is the sum of risk probability for all items i , and the revised equation for predicted failures follows:

Eq 8-12:
$$PredictedFailures = \sum_{i=1}^{N} \frac{(F(ai + ui) - F(ai))}{(1 - F(ai))}$$

Example: Assume a fleet of 12 identical cars described by Table 8-1 has a predominant early life water pump failure mode. The manufacturer indicates the failure distribution is Weibull with β=1.5 and η = 25000 miles. A typical car in the fleet increases mileage by 800 miles per month. (continued)

159

Perform a future risk analysis without replacement/repair and determine the following:

- Expected number of failures between now and 12 months in the future.

- End period projected 12 month repair cost for water pumps assuming $350 per repair

Solution: The CDF describing probability of failure for one water pump:

Eq 8-13

$$CDF: F(x) = 1 - \frac{1}{\left(e^{\left(\frac{x}{25000}\right)^{1.5}}\right)}$$

For each car, the "perceived now mileage," and mileage at evaluation time are:

Figure 8-5: Study Initial Conditions

	A	B	C	D
1		ai	ui	ai+ui
2	Car	Now Mileage	Added Miles	Miles @ Eval
3	1	5000	9600	14600
4	2	5000	9600	14600
5	3	7000	9600	16600
6	4	9000	9600	18600
7	5	9000	9600	18600
8	6	9000	9600	18600
9	7	11000	9600	20600
10	8	11000	9600	20600
11	9	11000	9600	20600
12	10	13000	9600	22600
13	11	15000	9600	24600
14	12	15000	9600	24600

F	G	H	I	J	K
		Eq 8-1		Eq 8-1	Eq 8-10
Car	ai+ui	F(ai+ui)	ai	F(ai)	[F(ai+ui)-F(ai)]/[1-F(ai)]
1	14600	0.360	5000	0.086	0.30
2	14600	0.360	5000	0.086	0.30
3	16600	0.418	7000	0.138	0.32
4	18600	0.474	9000	0.194	0.35
5	18600	0.474	9000	0.194	0.35
6	18600	0.474	9000	0.194	0.35
7	20600	0.527	11000	0.253	0.37
8	20600	0.527	11000	0.253	0.37
9	20600	0.527	11000	0.253	0.37
10	22600	0.577	13000	0.313	0.38
11	24600	0.623	15000	0.372	0.40
12	24600	0.623	15000	0.372	0.40
				Expected Failure Sum=	4.25

Figure 8-6: Completed Risk Analysis by Spreadsheet:

Answers:

- The expected number of water pump failures is given by Fig 8-6 Cell K13 Total

- We expect 4 or 5 water pumps to fail within the next 12 month period.

- We would expect the cost to be 4.25 * $350 each = $1487.50 total

Optional Material: Reasonableness Check: We can sometimes do a reasonableness check based on our general understanding of Weibull. Consider the following:

- A Weibull PDF with η=25000 will have 63% of its area prior to x=25000

- A Weibull PDF with β=1.5 will be a fairly wide distribution starting at x=0

The PDF will likely look something like this:

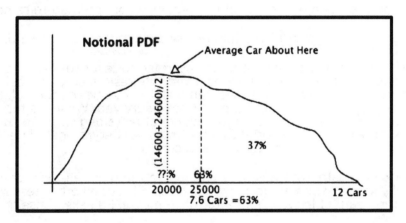

Figure 8-7: Analysis Estimate

The typical car remaining in our fleet will have about 20000 miles at the Risk Evaluation point i.e. (14000+25000)/2. This is somewhat less than the η value of 25000 where 63% of failures are expected.

Our risk analysis was analysis without repairs (meaning we parked broken cars beside the road). By totaling column J of Figure 8-6, about 2.7 cars are parked with failure at start of analysis leaving a fleet of 9.3 cars. Based on the position of our dotted line representing "Average Car in Fleet" I would guess about 50% of the remaining cars will have water-pump problems. 50% of the remaining 9.3 cars is 4.7 cars. This estimated value is in the "ball-park" of the calculated 4.25 failures.

Optional: Weibull Rank Number Adjustment by Future Risk:

Chapter 3 presented 3 methods for adjusting actual failure sequence numbers of data-points when the data includes "discarded data-points." One of those methods was Watson's Weibull Rank Adjustment method which uses future risk to determine the likelihood of a discarded sample failing prior to subsequent actual failures. Watson's method will now be explained as a Future Risk application.

During Engineering Life testing of equipment, multiple samples are subjected to a test environment to measure progressive failure times. Often, one or more samples are removed prematurely and are called Discards (or suspensions). When time of removal is known, such premature removal time does affect life conclusions because there exists calculable probability of a discard failing prior to the next actual failure. In consequence, the failure sequence number of the following failure should be "bumped up" by adding that probability. The analysis rapidly becomes more complex because there also exists a calculable probability of the discard failing prior to the 2nd and 3rd ... post failures. Thus a chain of "bump up" values from a single discard cascades throughout all subsequent actual failures.

When discussing discard data, there are two relevant points of view.

- How might a test sample see its life expectancy post premature removal?

- How might the analyst adjust actual failure count subsequent to a discard?

If the reader will indulge names and emotions ascribed to test samples, the following results. Test widget Ed (from table below) believed "life test" a cruel imposition intended to force his demise. He considers early test removal to have been merciful. Having been spared, Ed ponders how much longer he might have survived. While his future was uncertain, he realizes he can use the future risk equation (along with the "death" CDF) to calculate the likelihood of "death" prior to later times. Anxiety prone Ed decides to compute his life chances compared to his fallen comrades.

Consider the following data, where Wanda, Ed, Joe and Tom are all widgets in a life test. Ed was mercifully saved (when an accelerometer fell off) but all other test widgets failed in test. Seeing the death of Joe and Tom after his removal, Ed asks himself:

- What is the likelihood I would have died before Joe?

- What is the likelihood I would have died before Tom?

	Widget	Time	Status
1	Wanda	22	Fail
2	Ed	28	Discard
3	Joe	42	Fail
4	Tom	68	Fail

Table 8-2: Widget Failure Results

Thus Ed would use the future risk equation to compute the probability of failure between his removal at 28 seconds and Joe's death at 42 seconds. Next, he would compute likelihood of failure between his 28 second removal and Tom's death at 68 seconds. This fairy tale recounts the thinking of Ed, the troubled test widget who was removed prematurely.

The Analyst has different concerns.

- Concerning the 3rd Test Sample (2nd Actual Failure): How much should the failure number be "bumped up" to compensate for probability of Ed's early removal?

- Concerning the 4th Test Sample (3rd Actual Failure): Same question about Ed's early removal.

The analyst needs the same two predictions that Ed is pondering.i.e.

- What is the probability of Discard at 28 seconds failing prior to actual 42 second failure?

- What is the probability of Discard at 28 seconds failing prior to actual 68 second failure?

Once computed, these "bump-up" values are simply added to the Fail number as shown below.

Sample	Time	Status	FailNo	AdjFailNo
1	22	Failure	1	1
2	28	Discard		
3	42	Failure	2	2+P(failure between 28 & 42)
4	68	Failure	3	3+P(failure between 28 & 68)

Table 8-3: Data-point Failure Risk Adjustments

Adjusted Failure Numbers of table above can be used for Weibull Analysis in lieu of the Fail Number. When is done, the total number of points is unchanged (still 4) because these Adjusted Fail Numbers represent position based on a 4 sample population.

The Analyst thus needs to know how much to "bump up" each Actual Fail number; but, the question arises, "If multiple Discards occur prior to an Actual Failure, how should they be applied as "bump ups?" Also, "After a Discard bumps up the next failure, is it done; or does it cascade through all subsequent failures?" In response, a discarded test sample cascades "bump-up" to all subsequent failures. When an actual failure is preceded by multiple discards, "bump-ups" will result from each of the prior discards.

Watson's Rank Adjustment Method Demonstrated:

Watson's Rank Adjustment method is a direct application of the future risk without replacement equation. Imagine a data-set consisting of 5 data-points, which includes 2 Discards as below. Data-points 1, 3 and 5 are real Fail locations (Actual Failures).

The example is presented below to demonstrate Watson's Rank Adjustment. Because the example involving "Ed the troubled widget", does not include multiple discards, a more complex example will be worked based on the following data-set.

Data Point	Time	Status	Actual Fail No
1	15	Failure	1
2	29	Discard	
3	42	Failure	2
4	68	Discard	
5	96	Failure	3

Table 8-4: Example Problem Failure Data

Step 1: Use the Lenard Jones Rank adjustment method followed by a Weibull Plot to determine initial estimates of β and η as shown: β = 1.175   η = 81.34

Step 2: Use CDF Equation to determine probabilities for time=29, 42, 68 and 96

■ PDF Area from 0 to 29:   .2574

■ PDF Area from 0 to 42:   .3687

■ PDF Area from 0 to 68:   .5552

■ PDF Area from 0 to 96:   .7033

Step 3: Determine "bump-ups" for real failures based on Eq 8-7:

■ 1st Fail: no prior discards: bump-up = 0

■ 2nd Fail bump-up from 29   bump-up=[F(t+u)-F(t)]/[1-F(t)]=[.3687-.2574]/[1-.2574]=.15

■ 3rd Fail bump-up from 29   bump-up=[F(t+u)-F(t)]/[1-F(t)]=[.7033-.2574]/[1-.2574]=.6005

■ 3rd Fail bump-up from 68   bump-up=[F(t+u)-F(t)]/[1-F(t)]=[.7033-.5552]/[1-.5552]=.3330

164

Step 4 : Add "bump-ups" to each real Failure to get adjusted failure number.

Data-point	Time	F/D	Fail No	Fail+bump-up	
1	15	F	1	1	
2	29	D			
3	42	F	2	2+.15	From 29 sec
4	68	D			
5	96	F	3	3+.6005+.3320	29 & 68 sec

Table 8-5: Data-point Rank Adjustments

Step 5: Use updated data-set to create Weibull Plot based on N =5 & Benard's Eq:

Time (x)	AdjFailRank	Med%	Ln(x)	LnLn(1/(1-Med%))
15	1	.1296	2.7081	-1.9747
42	2.15	.3426	3.7377	-0.8688
96	3.9335	.6729	4.5643	0.1111

Table 8-6: Watson's Rank Adjustment Complete

Step 6: Create Weibull Plot to determine Beta & Eta from 2nd Pass Analysis:

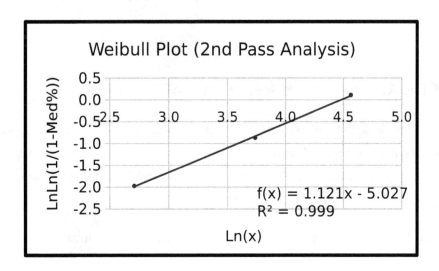

Figure 8-8: Weibull Plot - 2nd Pass Analysis

Results:

2nd Pass Analysis Result: $\beta = 1.121$ $\eta = 88.62$ R^2=99.9%

- Change in β from 1st Pass Analysis = 4.8%

- Change in η from 1st Pass Analysis = 8.2%

Discussion:

Analysis of data using Watson's Rank Order Adjustment requires a 2 pass analysis. The first pass is a Weibull Plot based on a modified Leonard Jones Rank Adjustment. The 2nd pass analysis uses 1st pass β and future risk equations to create better Adjusted Rank numbers before creating the 2nd pass Weibull Plot.

It should be recalled that the Leonard Jones adjustment method applies corrections based on Discard sequence relative to actual failure sequence. This means that a true failure at 20 seconds preceded by a discard at 19.9 seconds receives full benefit from the prior discard, despite the small likelihood of the discard maturing into failure in the prior tenth second. Watson's Weibull Rank Adjustment addresses this weakness.

For the example problem presented, the 2nd pass analysis resulted in 4.8% correction to β and 8.2% correction to η relative to the baseline Leonard Jones based analysis. The extent of improvement is likely significant only when extended future projections are made based on Weibull determinations. A preliminary study provided in Appendix F suggests random data-set variation is likely to introduce greater β uncertainty than created by use of either Leonard Jones or Bompas-Smith Rank Adjustment methods.

Future Risk Analysis With Replacement or Repair:

Future Risk Analysis with Replacement or Repair assumes failed units are returned to service either by replacement or repair. Consider two populations each of 100 items having η=2000. The first population is not repaired/replaced and the second is replaced on failure. After 2000 hours of operation, we will find the following:

- Group 1 (no repairs): In service population dwindled to 37 units.

- Group 2 (repair/replace); In service population 37 original units and 63 replacements.

166

Group 1 will have a reduced number of failures because there simply aren't many units left to fail. Group 2 has the same number of "worn out" units, but also 63 new units some of which will fail. It is an inescapable conclusion that Service Populations with Repair/Replace will have more failures than Service Populations which are allowed to dwindle in number.

The New Weibull Handbook states "... when the probability of failure in the interval in question is 0.5 or less, the risk with or without replacement is about the same. As the probability of failure is greater than about 0.5, the chance of more than one failure over the interval becomes significant."(3)

When the added probability of failure is significant, "the expected number of failures may be calculated by adding a new zero time unit whenever the future risk increases by a unit amount"(4)

In conclusion, the efficient closed form equation characterization of "Risk without repair/ replace" cannot be used in circumstances where failed units are returned to service (by whatever means). For analysis where failed units are returned to service, absence of closed form solution forces the analyst to rely on computer based simulation.

Chapter Summary:

Three general types of Risk Analysis have been presented. Two of the methods are based on an unmodified Weibull CDF equation aside from recognizing that various items in a fleet may have distinct service usage times. The Future Risk methods (both with and without repair/ replacements) require an additional CDF equation adjustment that scales up the percentage of failure between the initiation of study and time=infinity.

Chapter 8 Footnotes

1. Two Block Fox: The Rise of the Aircraft Carrier, by Charles M. Melhorn, US Naval Institute (c) 1974 Annapolis Maryland

2. Two Block Fox states that the mean time between failures for a rotary aircraft engine of the 1930s was about 250 hours. The Weibull η value representing 63% will be somewhat more than average and is assumed to be $\eta = 280$ hours. Given that high performance aircraft engines are complex devices, a fairly low β value of 1.5 is assumed. While making an interesting example, the reader should be aware that application of Weibull Equations to the multitude of possible engine failure modes is not recommended.

3. The New Weibull Handbook, Dr. Robert B. Abernethy (c) 1993 Eq 4-2 page 4-3

4. Ibid, p4-4

5. Coasters, An Illustrated History, by Roy Fenton, Seaforth Publishing, © 2011 by the author.

6. Weibull Analysis of coastal freighter service life was performed by the author on a sample of 30 coastal freighters in service between 1870 and 1960. The study determined $\beta=2.64220$ and $\eta=49.99$. The R^2 value was 95.4%. The most common cause for loss was wrecked at sea.

7. Why might we analyze Interval between earthquakes rather than year vs. earthquake? Earthquakes do not "respect" human conventions regarding calendar year. Because geologic time moves very slowly, it is to be expected that earthquake frequency is constant. Using time between earthquakes provides a single stream of objective earthquake data needed by Weibull Analysis.

At the heart of Weibull Analysis, a sorted single valued stream of observations is analyzed (not two variables such as calendar year vs. earthquake count.) For Weibull Analysis, Median Percent Theory (see chapter 3) is used to establish a "y" value for the purpose of plotting pseudo x vs. pseudo y and thus determining β and η.

Chapter 8 Homework:

1. Use Weibull Risk Analysis to determine the likelihood of a major off-shore earthquake on the Washington and Oregon coast. The concern is whether a major quake can be expected from the Cascadia Subduction Zone which is about 50 miles off shore.

Background. The earth has rigid plates that make up its surface and these move around a bit. Their rough edges get compressed like springs until something breaks loose and earth shakes like jello. The Juan De Fuca plate is moving northeast at 12 feet per century and is "buckling" beneath the American Plate. Intervals between major quakes is about 500 years.

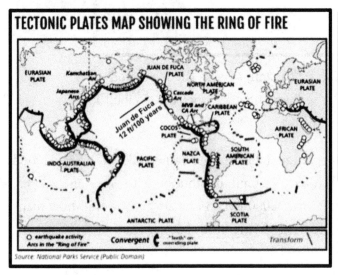

Approx Quake Date	Years Since Last
Jan 1700 AD	780
880-960 AD	210
550-750 AD	330
250-320 AD	910
610-450 BC	400
910-780 BC	250
1150-1220 BC	Unknown

See Atwater, et. al. (2003), Earthquake Recurrence Inferred .. Paleoseismology, Dev. in Quant.Sci.

Perform a risk analysis, documenting each of the following steps.

- Use data from the table above to perform a spreadsheet based Weibull Plot to determine β and η for the Cascadia Subduction Zone. (see Note 7)

- Write the CDF equation which incorporates β and η you determined in above.

- The last Cascadia Earthquake occurred in 1700. We are now in year 2021. The interval of time since the last is 321 years.

- Perform future risk using "a" = 321 years. Compute probability of a quake in 50 years.

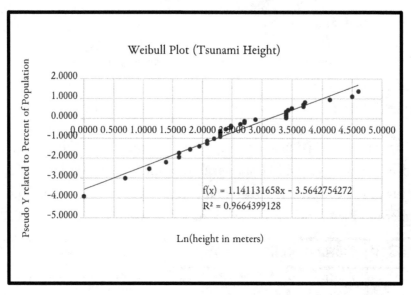

Weibull Plot (Tsunami Height)

$f(x) = 1.141131658x - 3.5642754272$
$R^2 = 0.9664399128$

Y axis: Pseudo Y related to Percent of Population

X axis: Ln(height in meters)

2. If Galveston Island in Texas is struck by a Tsunami, what is the likelihood of the wave being less than 15.2 meters (50 feet) tall? Use β and η values from the Weibull Plot: β=1.14113 and η=22.7 meters.

3. A rental car business has 7 economy import cars (all the same brand and 1997). Single mode failure of the "door handle" can be described by a Weibull distribution with β = 7 and η = 3.5. If a Present Risk Analysis is performed in January 2000 (when cars are 3 years old), how many door handle failures are expected to have occurred for the fleet of seven cars?

- Show all equations and major steps.

- In less than ¼ page, explain why you expected, or did not expect this result.

4. Historical information from the Journal of the US Artillery indicates the following gun barrel life. (Gun barrel life was expressed by the number of rounds fired before the bore became unserviceable). Examine the table below. Feel free to use a calculator or make a sketch if it helps you.

- If life is described by Weibull, what is your "estimate/guess" of the η value?

- In less than 1/8 page, explain why you think that.

Size (in)	Rounds	Manufacturer	Data Source	FailMode
2.25	472	Unknown	JUSA1895p739	Bore Wear
10	275	CrozierWire	JUSA1903p8	Bore Wear
8	390	WatervlietArm	JUSA1903p13	Bore Wear
8	335	WestpoiintFnd	Ditto	Bore Wear
8	388	WestpointFnd	Ditto	Barrel Crack
10	281	WatervlietArm	Ditto	Bore Wear
12	265	WatervlietArm	Ditto	Bore Wear
12 Mortar	398	Unknown	Ditto	Bore Wear
12 Mortar	399	Unknown	Ditto	Bore Wear

5. You are a British citizen in the time of Queen Victoria, the year 1895. You are asked to project the expected loss of coastal trading ships for your family's shipping company. From 1850 through 1940, there were many British companies that managed small coastal trading freighters. They carried passengers, coal, grain and many other things to coastal communities. Most of these ships were between 150 and 250 feet long. By the 1930's they looked like this:

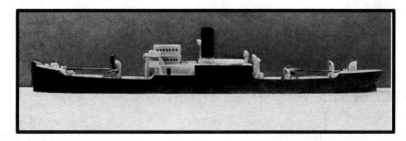

A study of 30 historical coastal freighters indicates their service life could be modeled by a Weibull Distribution with β=2.64 and η=50 years (4,5). In 1900, your family business purchased four ships with ages shown below.

Ship	Age at Purchase
Claymore	12 years
St Paul	20 years
Isle of Mann	20 years
Texa	30 years

- Estimate the probable number of ships that will be lost within 20 years

- Estimate the probable number of ships remaining in service at the end of 20 years.

Chapter 9: Weibull vs. R&M Crossroads:

A primary emphasis of this book is determination of Weibull parameters that describe a population based on a data-set. Detailed methods have been provided. For the R&M engineer, combining these methods with Chapter 9 information provides a direct and convincing path for determining various R&M parameters (such as time dependent Hazard Rate) from a raw data-set. This is a major R&M benefit from understanding Weibull Analysis.

During equipment design, Reliability and Maintainability (R&M) organizations influence design decisions, monitor post delivery failures and craft maintenance programs. Chapter 9 is intended to help R&M Engineers understand Weibull in the context of their own discipline. While brief definitions and discussions are provided below, more comprehensive explanations may be found in "Mechanical Survival: the use of reliability data" by J. H. Bompas-Smith (1)

Justifying Use of the Weibull Distribution:

Many analysts wonder how they can justify using Weibull as opposed to some other distribution such as the Exponential or the Gaussian Distributions. The answer is pragmatic and not unlike a mechanic's decision to use a particular wrench. Weibull is used when the Weibull Plot fits the data-set. Weibull Analysis is almost always accompanied by a Weibull Plot, and is usually better justified than is the practice with competing distributions.

Theory can rarely justify use of a particular distribution; but there are exceptions.

- In the late 1800's Austrian Physicist Ludwig Boltzman developed a statistical basis for analyzing entropy enabling creation of several useful engineering equations. His statistical work "provided the descriptive link between ... observation of nature and the microscopic view (2)"

- Various problems described by the binomial distribution are easily justified by demonstrating standard binomial assumptions apply.

While a few other exceptions exist, choice of statistical distribution to model a data-set is usually pragmatic. A distribution is used that fits the data and enables useful calculations.

Using Weibull for Complex Machines & Multimode Failure:

Previous chapters expressed a preference for single failure mode Weibull analysis; however, the Reliability and Maintainability (R&M) community is best positioned to evaluate their productive use of analysis methods. Weibull analysis of complex, multi-failure mode machines does raise concerns regarding β parameter inferences for machine improvement and maintenance programs; however, R&M organizations best understand their goals.

R&M Metrics

This book has consistently used x, for the variable of interest. The R&M community is interested in reliability change with time, and age is usually expressed as t. Chapter 9 will do likewise. R&M organizations apply several unique mathematical concepts in order to:

- Define/demonstrate contract requirements/compliance

- Analyze ongoing failure behavior.

It is thus convenient to have a summary that enables conversion of Weibull parameters into common R&M metrics. Examples follow:

- Reliability as a function of time

- Mortality or Failure Rate as a function of time

- Hazard Rate (Local Failure Rate) as a function of time

Analysis and equations that follow assume a population of devices put into service without repair or replacement. For fielded equipment populations that include repair or replacement, the equations that follow must be adjusted. In many such cases, closed form equivalents do not exist.

Reliability of a Device R(t):

By definition, "the Reliability of a device is the probability that an item will perform satisfactorily for a specified period of time under defined operating conditions."(3) Reliability usually varies with age, and is therefore expressed as a function of time: Reliability = R(t)

An example of an R&M statistic is the reliability that a male human will operate when called upon (i.e. will still be alive). Statistical data for the US in 2016 was used to create the CDF graph below showing time dependent reliability.

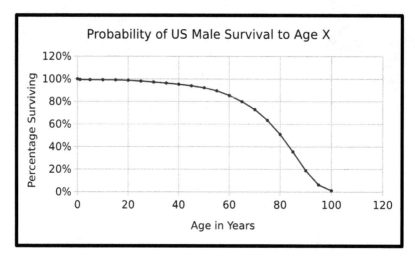

Figure 9-1: 2016 R(t) for US Male Survival

As an example, the graph shows that reliability for t=80 years indicates 50% survival of the original population. This can be interpreted as either 50% of the original population will still be functional, or equivalently as a 50% chance that a particular man will still be functional when he reaches that age. If a Weibull distribution is assumed, the CDF equation computes the percentage of "failures" by any time t. Since probability of failure + probability non-failure = 100%, we may compute Reliability R(t):

$$\text{Eq 9-1} \qquad R(t) = 1 - CDF = \; > 1 - \left[1 - \frac{1}{e^{\left(\left(\frac{t}{\eta}\right)^{\beta}\right)}} \right] = \frac{1}{e^{\left(\left(\frac{t}{\eta}\right)^{\beta}\right)}}$$

Example: Determine Reliability at t = 15 years for a Weibull distribution with β=2 and η=10:

R(15) = e ^ -[(15/10)]^2 = 2.718 ^ -1.52 = .1054 = 10.54% Reliability at 15 years

Un-Reliability of a Device F(t):

By definition, Unreliability of a device is the probability that an item won't perform satisfactorily for a specified period of time. It is thus the cumulative Failure Probability and is the same as the CDF. For humans, the Unreliability curve is the mortality curve as it describes the percent of humans who will die by a specified age. Because the aged fair less well, unreliability is a function of age t and F(t) denotes probability of failure by time t. As observed by Bompas-Smith, the Unreliability or Failure curve "is exactly an upside down reliability curve" and is shown below for US males.

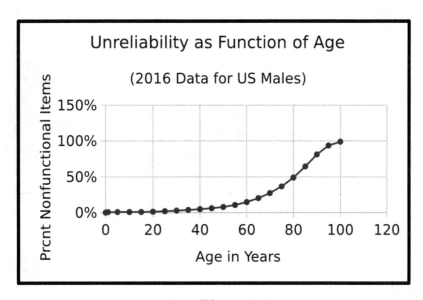

Figure 9-2: f(t) Unreliability

175

In sufficient quantity, raw data allows creation of R(t) which can also be modeled by Weibulll mathematics. The probability that an item will not function when called upon, is described by the CDF curve and thus failure probability F(t) for a two parameter Weibull Distribution of known β and η is:

Eq 9-2

$$CDF:F(t) = 1 - e^{\left(-\left(\frac{t}{\eta}\right)^{\beta}\right)}$$

There is always some risk Weibull modeling may deviate somewhat from actual raw data. A two parameter Weibull Analysis (using 9 data-points) from the US Male age survival data was performed to create Figure 9-3. Distortions of the Weibull CDF Fig 9-3 indicate measurable population survival out to 110 years, which is not true of the underlying data shown by Fig 9-2. This kind of analysis induced distortion could be tragic for an insurance company. Please compare Figures 9-2 and 9-3.

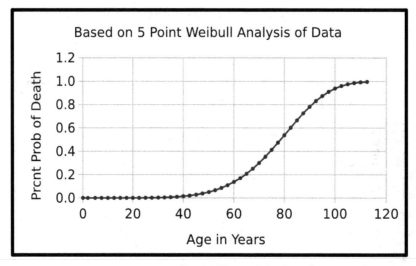

Figure 9-3: 2 Parameter Weibull Model of Male Mortality

Optional: The Male Mortality CDF Fig 9-3 is based on a Weibull Plot which exhibits "arced data-points", usually indicating a need for 3 parameter analysis. Appendix L presents this analysis and demonstrates that in this case, a 3 parameter analysis produces terrible results. Interested readers are referred to Appendix L for a full discussion.

The PDF of a Device f(t):

The PDF has been discussed many times. The PDF is the rate of accumulation of percent failures based on very small chunks of time. The PDF value is computed based on the original population size. Population failure count is low at the left of a PDF graph thus the PDF reflects a small percent of the original population. For Weibull distributed failure, the PDF equation, expressed using time t as the independent variable is:

Eq 9-3

$$2ParameterPDF: f(t) = \beta \cdot \frac{t^{(\beta-1)}}{\eta^{\beta}} \cdot e^{\left(-\left(\frac{t}{\eta}\right)^{\beta}\right)}$$

The PDF has been included for completeness and also because it is used to develop the R&M expression for Weibull based Hazard Rate. The Weibull based PDF graph for US Male Mortality in 2016 follows:

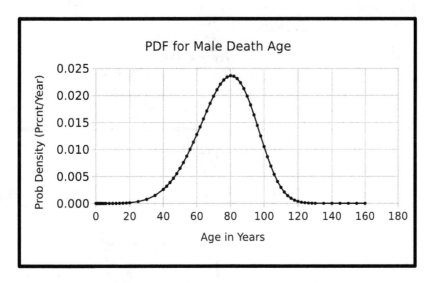

Figure 9-4: PDF of US Male Death Age

The Weibull based Male Death Age PDF has significant area above x=100 years that is absent in the original government data-set, thus forcing a distorted Weibull population description. This observation is consistent with the previous discussion.

Hazard Rate of a Machine or a Device H(t):

A wealthy man once lost half his fortune. A few years later, he lost half his fortune yet again. At the end of this time, was he "dead broke," or did he retain 25% of his fortune? If reported losses were in terms of the original fortune, then he was left "dead broke". However, if he lost 50% of his fortune in the first encounter and subsequently lost half of remainder, he was left with 25% of his original fortune. This illustrates the difference between reporting losses against initial vs. against local conditions. The crux of hazard rate is local reporting of failures in contrast to the PDF which reports against initial conditions.

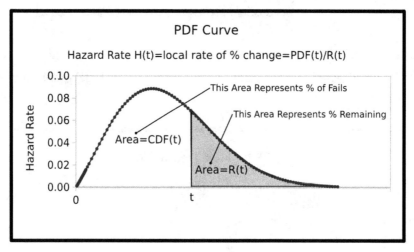

Figure 9-5: Typical PDF

The Hazard Rate H(t) equation for a 2 parameter Weibull population with known β and η:

$$\text{Eq 9-4} \qquad H(t) = \beta \cdot \frac{t^{(\beta-1)}}{\eta^{\beta}}$$

The PDF describes percent/time based on total population. The Hazard Function describes percent/time based on remaining population (and is computed by dividing the PDF by (1-CDF) (5)(6)). For small values of t, the remaining population and the total population are

178

about the same, so the left of Figure 9-6 shows correspondence of PDF and H(t). For large t values, Hazard Rate losses relative to the very scarce remaining items magnifies the Hazard Rate and its value far exceeds the PDF value.

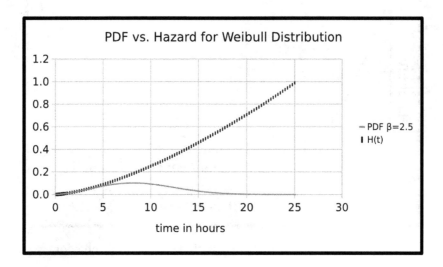

Figure 9-6: PDF vs. Hazard Rate

Conclusion for R&M Metrics:

Reliability and Maintainability Engineers use a number of mathematical equations suited to their discipline. After determination, Weibull parameters β and η are easily converted into many of these R&M metrics. Weibull analysis thus provides a well defined and efficient way of reducing equipment data to desired R&M statistics.

Complex Machines and the Lifetime Failure Model:

Product life behavior of complex machines is often conceptualized by the bath-tub failure model. The illustration below represents a product which exhibits numerous early failures, followed by a consistent service period. As the product ages, it reaches a "wear-out" stage during which failures are increasingly frequent.

179

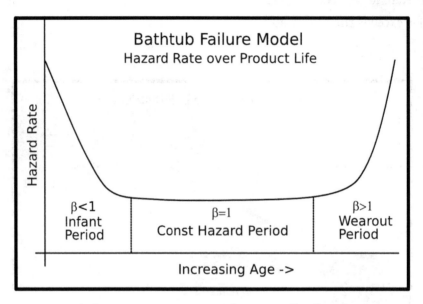

Figure 9-7: Common Conceptualization of Life Behavior

The commonly used bath-tub failure model for complex machines seems consistent with experience. A new car often has minor problems before settling into a prolonged period of dependable performance. After 100K miles, things begin to change. A multitude of failures ranging from door handles to water pumps become common until vehicle replacement.

Constant Failure Rate, Weibull & Exponential Distribution:

The Bath-tub failure distribution is of interest because:

- The bath-tub failure model is the most common conceptualization for failure behavior of complex machines.

- The constant hazard period (horizontal portion of Figure 9-7) enables use of simplified R&M equations; but, these are strictly justified only when the Weibull β = 1. Simplified R&M equation use is thus tied to Weibull Analysis.

The reader should note that Figure 9-7 is about hazard rate and not failure rate (7). By definition, Hazard Rate is the PDF divided by the remaining viable units and is denoted R(t) (8). For a Weibull Distribution, we can derive the Hazard Rate Equation 9-5 as follows:

$$\text{Eq 9-5:} \quad H(t) = f(t)/R(t) = \boxed{H(t) = \beta \cdot \frac{t^{(\beta-1)}}{\eta^{\beta}}}$$

The central portion of the bath-tub model is constant; therefore, we should examine the Weibull Hazard Rate equation and ask, "What conditions cause this to be a constant?" Because β and η are numbers, scrutiny falls on $t^{(\beta-1)}$. The Hazard Rate can only be constant at all values of t when β equals one. For these conditions, the Weibull Equation simplifies to equations 9-6 and 9-7.

$$\text{Eq 9-6} \qquad \boxed{WeibPDF\ const - hazard: \frac{1}{\eta} \cdot e^{\left(-\left(\frac{1}{\eta}\right) \cdot t\right)}}$$

For convenience, λ is defined as $1/\eta$ yielding the familiar Exponential Distribution Equation:

$$\text{Eq 9-7: Exponential Distribution Equation} \qquad \boxed{f(t) = \lambda \cdot e^{(-\lambda \cdot t)}}$$

When equipment reliability can be represented as a Weibull with $\beta=1$ then:

The Weibull equation reduces to exponential equation 9-7 above. In such cases, it is always true that λ of the exponential distribution is equal to the reciprocal of the Weibull η.

Failure exhibits a constant hazard rate for the horizontal portion of the bath tube curve represented by the exponential equation.

Mean Time Between Failure (MTBF)- What and Why:

The MTBF is a commonly used parameter quantifying the unreliability of a machine or component. It supposedly represents the average time between failures for a machine and is often stated as a single numeric value such as 20,000 hours MTBF. Usually, machine MTBF is analytically computed based on piece part reliability data-bases and the resulting MTBF is computed without awareness or concern for time dependency of overall machine failure. The reader is cautioned that the great majority of equipment has failure characteristics that do vary with time. The MTBF becomes a single number (invariant with age of device) only when special conditions result in a flat portion of the bath-tub curve as discussed above. When failure is described as a Weibull Distribution, this can only occur when β=1. (19)

Looking at various equations (PDF, CDF, R(t) etc.), one cannot help wondering "Where is the MTBF? How is it represented within the various equations and graphs? How do I know?"

Eq 9-8

Alternative Form:

$$MTBF = 1/\lambda$$
$$MTBF = \eta weib$$

Optional Material: Estimating the Value of MTBF:

If Constant Hazard Rate applies (i.e. Weibull β=1), η is the MTBF and constant.

If Hazard Rate H(t) varies with time, there exists some average behavior over the interval. It seems reasonable to wonder whether η approximates the MTBF for β values other than one. A. D. S. Carter identifies means of computing MTBF using the Gamma Function as follows (9)(10):

Eq 9-9

$$MTBF = \eta \cdot \Gamma\left(1 + \frac{1}{\beta}\right)$$

The above equation was used to compute MTBF/η as a function of β with the following result.

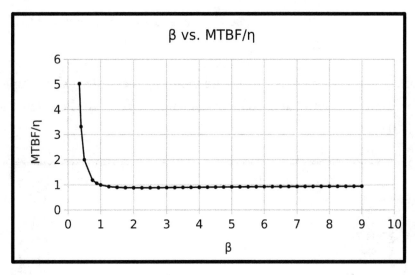

Figure 9-8: MTBF in Dimensionless Form

From the figure, it is apparent that:

- For $\beta=1$, the MTBF is precisely the Weibull η parameter and does not change with time.

- For $\beta>1$, the Weibull η value is a reasonable approximation for MTBF; but, the local MTBF does have time dependence.

- For $\beta<1$, the MTBF cannot be estimated based on η

Maintainability and the Weibull β Parameter:

When a Weibull Analysis is performed on a single mechanism of failure or a component with limited modes of failure, the Weibull β parameter often indicates the nature of underlying causes of failure and the likely remediation. This does not apply at the complex machine level and when so applied is likely to misdirect corrective actions.

- Only when applied at the failure mechanism level, three regimes (Weibull $\beta<1$, $\beta=1$, $\beta>1$) typically indicate whether poor design, poor manufacturing control or poor maintenance is the predominant cause of failure. When Weibull is applied to complex, multi-mode machines, this is no longer true, and such interpretation will likely result in failed remedial efforts.(11)

- "The often used bath-tub lifetime failure model applies only at the complex machine level, rarely at the individual component and almost never to the failure mechanism level." (12)

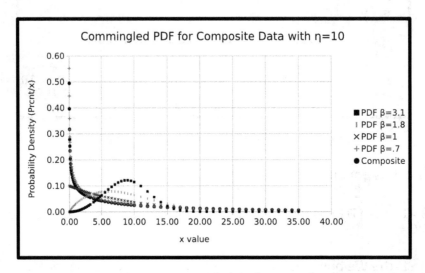

Figure 9-9: Commingled Failure Mechanisms

Figure 7-9 repeated above shows the Weibull results of modeling a complex machine having multiple failure modes with βs ranging from .7 to 3. When combined into a single data-set and analyzed, the resulting β=.819 incorrectly implies need for increased maintenance, or increased scrutiny of piece parts. Neither of these strategies would effectively address underlying design issues.

While β inferred strategies for mitigating failures at the component level are appropriate, application of β inferred strategies to commingled failure mechanisms of complex machines is not recommended. It often leads to inappropriate corrective action.

Various commercial software can perform Weibull Analysis. Recognizing the R&M need to address machine level failure, some enable analysis of multi-mode failure at the machine level. Such gross generalizations are likely to be correct; but conclusions should be limited to the expected failure behavior of the machine. Inference of production issues related to quality, design and maintenance should not be based on commingled failure mode analyses.

Weibull β indications of remediation for single mode failure:

<u>β substantially less than 1</u>: This condition is often called infant mortality. In such circumstance, the distribution of failure decreases over time and typically results from either of two causes.

- "Poor quality control in the manufacturing process or some other mechanism which permits the installation of low quality components" (13).

- "Inadequate standard of maintenance activity. By inadequate standard, a lack of effectiveness rather than effort is indicated." (14)

When $\beta<<1$, reliability increases with age and thus replacement at set intervals to address issues is counterproductive. "Burn in screening" of new components is sometimes used as a mitigation method.

<u>β approximately 1</u>: "When single mode of failure shape parameter (β) has a value of approximately one, the Weibull analysis indicates that constant hazard conditions apply."(15) When constant hazard rate is real, single valued MTBF is meaningful & not time dependent.

- Equipment which predominantly exhibits constant hazard over working life should not replaced at set life points since, by definition, the replacement has the same … instantaneous probability of failure as the replaced item.(16)

- A clear distinction should be made between component failure mechanisms and complex machines. For complex machines "Frequently, an equipment item will appear to exhibit constant hazard because it has several failure modes of a variety of types, none of which dominant. … The difficulty here is that the counter-strategy for the individual failure modes may be significantly different to those suggested by the constant hazard conditions for the system or equipment as a whole. "(17)

- When a true constant hazard condition applies, de-rating, redundancy or modification of design are appropriate strategies for product improvement.

β Substantially Greater than 1: When Weibull β is greater than one (at the failure mechanism level of detail) it indicates the hazard rate increases over time and is associated with wear-out failure modes (18). If wear-out occurs within the intended usage life of equipment, it is of concern and is best addressed through feature/material redesign or by preventative maintenance. Planned replacement of aged units is an appropriate strategy if it is economically and technically feasible.

Conclusion for Maintenance and Weibull:

When Weibull Analysis is applied at the failure mechanism level of detail, Weibull shape factor β, often provides an indication of the cause of failure and can be used as a basis for investigation or for establishing mitigation strategies. But when Weibull Analysis is applied to complex, multi-failure mode machines, very often Weibull β from commingled failure causes incorrectly indicates "infant mortality" despite reality of multiple wear-out modes of failure. Development of a maintenance strategy based on misplaced belief is ineffective and costly.

The R&M community is best positioned to determine how best they can apply Weibull and other methods to achieve their goals; however, the following cautions are noted.

- Production and quality changes should not be based on Weibull β value inference from commingled failure modes.

- Weibull Analysis of complex machines should be applied only for well defined and understood purposes.

- Like all analyses, analysts using Weibull should have a thorough understanding of the assumptions "built into" the various analysis engines to ensure that a particular analysis is applicable to the circumstance at hand.

Chapter Footnotes:

1. Readers are referred to Mechanical Survival: the use of reliability data, by J. H. Bompas-Smith, Edited by R.H.W. Brook. Bompas-Smith provides clear explanations for R&M.

2. Quotation from Entropy (statistical thermodynamics) as posted on Wikipedia, en.wikipedia.org March 2021,

3. Op. Cit, Bompas-Smith, "Mechanical Survival" p1

4. Underlying Public Domain data from Social Security Website www.ssa.gov for year 2016.

5. Op. Cit., Bompas-Smith, "Mechanical Survival", p8

6. Also identified in itl.nist.gov website regard Failure (or hazard) rate

7. See The Use of Weibull in Defect Data Analysis, as posted on https://warwick.ac.uk, March 2021. Original article dated 2004, p7

8. Op. Cit., Bompas-Smith, "Mechanical Survival", p 7

9. The Gamma Function: Op. Cit. A.D.S. Carter, "Mechanical Survival", p37

10. The Gamma Function: "The New Weibull Handbook", Dr. Abernethy page 2-4

11. Op. Cit. Bompas-Smith, "Mechanical Survival", p7

12. Op. Cit. https://warwick.ac.uk, "The Use of Weibull in Defect Analysis p12

13. Ibid p7

14. Ibid p7

15. Ibid p8

Ibid p8

Ibid p8

18 Ibid p8

16. Ibid p8

17. Ibid p8

18 Ibid p8

19. Excellent discussion is provided by Warwick Group. The discussion here-in is heavily influenced by their excellent report. See foot note 12.

Homework Chapter 9:

1. If failure for population of machines can be described by a Weibull Distribution having β=3.5 and η=30, write the equation for the Reliability R(t) function.

2. For the same population described in problem 1 above:

- Write down the equation for the cumulative failures at time t (hint: this is the CDF)

- Use a spreadsheet to create a graph of the cumulative failure percent. Hint: for x value of the graph, use t= .25, .50, .75, 1, 2, 4, 6, 10, 20, 30, 40, 60, 80, 100

- Compute the population expected value of percent failures at time t = 18

3. For the same population, write the equation for the Hazard Rate H(t) equation.

4. If failure of an electronic diode can be described by a Weibull Equation with β= 1 and η=90000, what is the MTBF of the diode?

5. If rivet failure can be described by a Weibull Distribution having β=.2 and η=35,

- What is the likely design/manufacturing issue and why do you think so?

- What do you think should be done about this?

6. If flexible drive shaft failure is described by β=5.2 and η=500 operation cycles:

- Is it meeting a contract requirement for 2000 operation cycles?

- What is the failure mode? (infant or wear-out?)

- If it is not contract compliant, what should be done about this?

7. If the life of a generator bearing is characterized by a Weibull Distribution with β=3.5 and η=5000 hours is not meeting contract life requirements, what do you think should be done about the bearing?

8. For a light bulb who's life is described by a Weibull with β=1 and η=542, write an equivalent exponential distribution equation describing the light bulb life phenomena.

Chapter 10: Three Parameter Weibull Equations:

Are Real Populations described by the Weibull Distribution?

The Weibull-DR analysis software manual states "Most real world distributions are rarely Weibull, and neither are they precisely Gaussian, binomial or exponential," but they conform closely enough to some standard distribution that statistical analysis provides useful insight and predictions. I agree with this viewpoint.

There is one class of "Weibull Misbehavior" that merits special attention. Certain real world phenomena are described very well by a Weibull which is offset by fixed "x" amount (either left or right). The graph below illustrates a group of Weibull PDFs having various β values and beginning at x=0, but also displays the same PDFs off-set by an amount I will call Xo (Tee-zero or Gamma by other authors). For the example below, Xo=15. Note: Xo and xo will be used interchangeably in Chapter 10.

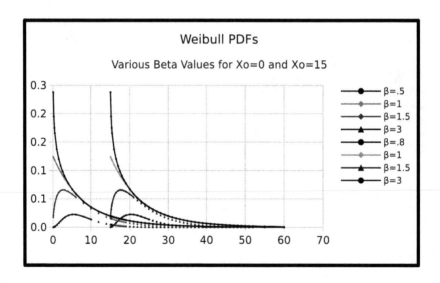

Figure 10-1: Weibull PDFs with Xo=0 vs Xo=15

From Figure 10-1 is apparent that Xo =15 "slides" the PDF plot to the right by 15 units. Real world data has no particular fondness for 15, and such real world offset can take on whatever Xo value enables Weibull description of real world data.

Chapter 7 discusses some of the things that can go wrong during Weibull data analysis. One item of discussion was Weibull Plots with "curved arcs" of points about the fitted Weibull line. Such "arced" data often indicates the need for a nonzero Xo , and thus a 3 parameter Weibull model. The reader needs to realize "arced data" can result from a variety of causes (e.g. commingled data). When faced with "arced" data, the analyst should therefore try the 3 parameter Weibull and evaluate the results with vigilant awareness of other possible causes.

Discussion of 2 vs. 3 Parameter Phenomena:

Identification of a data-set as 2 parameter vs. 3 parameter is uncertain but usually consists of:

- Performing a Weibull Plot and examining the plot for "arced" data points about the straight line. Note that "Arced" data can arise from other causes.

- When 3 parameter analysis methods are practical, the data is modeled both ways and results compared. If the 3 parameter model produces reasonable results while eliminating "arced data" or "data drupe" at range extremes then the 3 parameter solution is preferred. Conversely, if the optimum parameter solution occurs when Xo is near zero, then the solution reduces to a 2 parameter distribution (there is no need for inclusion of the 3rd parameter Xo).

Example phenomena below are grouped by the evident need for 2 vs. 3 parameter analysis.

Two Parameter Phenomena:

- Kochi annual rainfall data from 2010 to 2019 appears consistent with Xo = 0.

- There are known historical periods when agricultural yield approached zero due to catastrophes. This suggests a yield distribution beginning at x=zero (Thus Xo=0).

Uncertain 2 vs. 3 Parameter Phenomena:

- Japan Earthquake data consisting of 200 data points (Figure 8-1) appears adequately modeled with Xo = 0; however, "data drupe" at extreme x values suggests possible improvement with use of a 3 parameter Weibull.

- Historical Tsunami data likewise exhibits extreme x range data sag. Conversely, it is evident that waves come in all sizes, and we should expect the Tsunami distribution to begin at zero height.

- While a 2 parameter Weibull appears to model Australian Tawney shark length, it seems likely there is some minimum size below which infant sharks don't survive. This suggests a 3 parameter Weibull may be helpful.

Three Parameter Phenomena:

- Failure of structural metal subject to cyclic loading is called metal fatigue. Metal fatigue is known to have a "threshold number of cycles," thus requiring a three parameter Weibull.

- COVID-19 death statistics indicate infected people under 25 rarely die. This suggests a need for an Xo parameter; but, even this may not enable effective characterization.

In practice, populations are usually analyzed by the expedient 2 parameter Weibull unless the Weibull Plot shows "arcing of data." The 3 parameter Weibull is usually reserved for such situations. But when analysts have ready access to Weibull Software, both analyses are often performed to determine whether the 3 parameter Weibull significantly improves data correlation.

As a personal note, Weibull-DR was installed on my PC to facilitate writing this book. Three parameter analysis is invoked and compared to 2 parameter analysis with a single "mouse click." I routinely perform and compare the results of 2 vs. 3 parameter analysis before modeling a problem.

The 3 Parameter Weibull Equation & Its Challenges:

The 3 Parameter Weibull Equations (PDF and CDF) follow:

Eq 10-1

$$PDF - 3parameter: f(x) = \left(\beta \cdot \frac{(X - Xo)^{(\beta - 1)}}{(\eta^\beta)} \right) \cdot \frac{1}{e^{\left(\left(\frac{(X - Xo)}{\eta} \right)^\beta \right)}}$$

Eq 10-2

$$CDF - 3parameter: F(x) = 1 - \frac{1}{e^{\left(\left(\frac{(X - Xo)}{\eta} \right)^\beta \right)}}$$

Note: Equations are often expressed in more compact form by using negative exponents. The author feels greater clarity results from above.

Assignment of Xo = 0 in the above reduces equations to standard 2 parameter Weibull forms.

While β and η for the 2 parameter Weibull are easily computed from the best fit Weibull Plot line, this method does not work for the 3 parameter Weibull. Three approaches enable determination of Xo.

- Use of spreadsheet: An additional column is added to the right of the x observed data column. Its values are computed as x value reduced by constant Xo. Trial and error enables analyst to find the Xo value that eliminates "arching" in the Weibull Plot.

- Semi-Graphic Method: A method developed by GM shown below provides a means of estimating the needed Xo value without reliance on Weibull Analysis software.

- Commercial Weibull Software: Commercial Weibull Software is recommended.

Three Parameter Weibull Estimation by Method 1:

Example of Method 1: A Weibull data spreadsheet similar to Figure 10-2 is used. Cell "100" is provided for "trial" Xo values, with different values inserted until the desired solution is found (i.e. arced data is eliminated). Several plots with different Xo values are shown below to demonstrate sensitivity of the method.

To evaluate "trial" values of Xo, the analyst creates a Weibull Plot (spreadsheet x-y graph) based on the right two columns of Figure 10-2. Xstar is a column of measured data-points. Column X is the corresponding Xstar value, diminished by "100" (or other assumed value) thus becoming the basis for Weibull Plot pseudo x values.

By using absolute cell references (e.g. C2), in column X, column X is instantly updated for new entries in cell C2. Likewise for columns to the right. If a graph has been made based on LN(x) and Yweib, most spreadsheets will also update the graph automatically. In practice, this results in a reasonably efficient way for an analyst to try various values of Xo until he/she finds an Xo number that eliminates data "arcing".

	A	B	C	D	E	F
1			Assumed Xo			DejaVuSANS
2			100			
3		**Xstar**	**X**	**Med%**	**Ln(X)**	**Yweib**
4	1	105.58	5.58	12.96%	1.7192	-1.9745
5	2	109.20	9.20	31.48%	2.2192	-0.9727
6	3	112.49	12.49	50.00%	2.5249	-0.3665
7	4	116.15	16.15	68.52%	2.7819	0.1448
8	5	121.45	21.45	87.04%	3.0657	0.7145

Figure 10-2: 3 Parameter Weibull Analysis Spreadsheet

On the facing page, three Weibull Plots are presented, with progressively increasing assumed Xo start point for the 3 parameter Weibull. The first graphs begins with Xo assumed as zero. As larger Xo are assumed, "data arc" becomes less, and estimated β changes radically. While R^2 values look good, these solutions are not because even a small data arc is unacceptable.

The correct solution (Xo=100) is presented by Figure 10-6. Also shown is Weibull Plot Figure 10-7 showing concave reversal when Xo is over estimated.

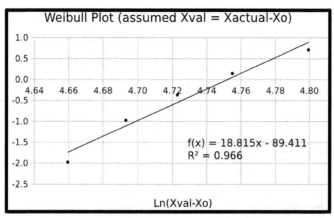

Figure 10-3: Xo assumed as 0

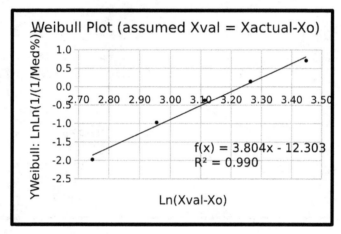

Figure 10-4: Xo assumed as 90.

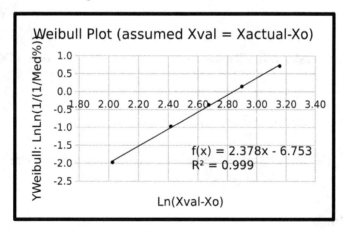

Figure 10-5: Xo assumed as 98

Figure 10-6 shows a very good straight line correlation because Xo was assumed as the correct value (Xo=100). The β value has dropped to 1.995 and η is now 15.01.

The author created the underlying data-set based on β=2 and η=15. Thus, this solution is known to be correct, and all indications from Figure 10-6 concur. During analysis of real world data-sets, some data-scatter will be present and the resulting R^2 value will be less than 100%. Also, the analyst wouldn't have have luxury of knowing the correct answer.

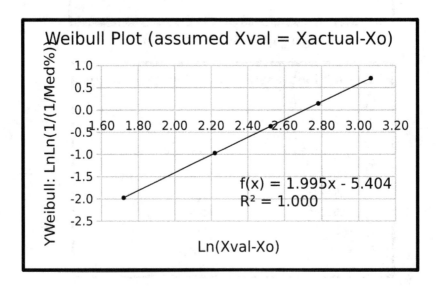

Figure 10-6: Xo assumed as 100

The reader may reasonably ask "What happens if I over estimate the value of Xo?" In response, I offer the following:

- Arced data will reoccur, but will become concave up as shown in Figure 10-7.

- If Xo exceeding the "smallest data-point" is assumed, the spreadsheet will issue error messages.

- The Weibull Plot assuming Xo=105 is provided by Figure 10-7.

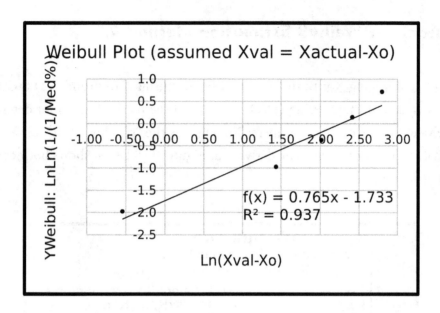

Figure 10-7: Xo assumed to exceed its actual value

Observations regarding Figure 10-7 :

- "Overshoot" of actual Xo value reverses concavity of arced data

- Rapid change in β estimate results

- Computed R^2 value rapidly deceases

- Assumed Xo left of the smallest actual data point results in spreadsheet errors

While technically possible, trial and error spreadsheet analysis is not recommended. Estimated Weibull parameters are very sensitive to changes in assumed Xo value, and thus the correct value must be accurately guessed. While use of absolute cell references (discussed earlier) speeds the process, an analyst may guess 50 times prior to closely approximating the true Xo. At some point, the mind simply "goes to sleep" and results become questionable.

Three Parameter Weibull Estimation Method 2:

Method 2 for Determining Xo: Both Warwick Manufacturing Group and A D S Carter Professor of Mechanical Engineering (1)(2) recommend the method below for determining the approximate value of the location parameter Xo which is the "starting point" for Weibull 3 parameter analysis. Carter presents the derivation. Figure 10-8 below shows both context and equation for estimating Xo.

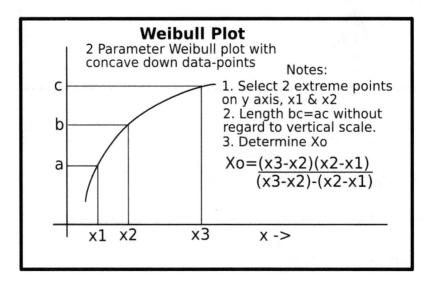

Figure 10-8: Xo Estimation Method

Three Parameter Weibull Estimation Method 3:

It is always easier to get work done if someone else does it for you and the same is true for estimating the 3 parameter Weibull off-set Xo parameter. Most commercial Weibull programs can perform this analysis. During the "trial use period" simply perform a 3 parameter test analysis using the Xstar data from Figure 10-2 . The program should compute close approximations to the following: $\beta=2$, $\eta=15$ and $Xo=100$ with $R^2 \sim 99.99\%$. These values are accurate because the Xstar data was created using Weibull Equations.

Current and Future Risk with a 3 Parameter Weibull

Risk calculations with the 3 Parameter Weibull can be approached in either of two ways:

- Method 1: After 3 parameter Weibull determination, the risk equations can be modified. Variable x is replaced by (x- Xo) in the risk equations.

- Method 2: After Weibull parameter determination, the entire risk analysis can be performed using x data-points decreased by value Xo. The future risk evaluation point is likewise decreased. Risk computations are then performed normally, but the analyst must realize that computed values refer to x values off-set by Xo.

Chapter 10 Conclusions:

When attempting to characterize a population based on data, concavity of the 2 parameter Weibull Plot usually indicates a need to apply 3 parameter Weibull Analysis to the data. Even slight concavity is important. When a 3 parameter Weibull population genuinely exists, the 3 parameter analysis often produces starkly different values for β and η.

- For life testing of newly designed equipment with dominant single mode failure mechanisms, a 3 parameter Weibull interpretation of experimental life data is sometimes essential. When wear-out failure modes dominate, clinging to a 2 parameter approach may force equipment redesign in circumstances where a 3 parameter Weibull analysis would have demonstrated sufficient life.

- Estimation of the Xo position parameter cannot be achieved by closed form solution. Trial and error using a spreadsheet is not a satisfactory solution. A D S Carter et. al. present a method summarized above which can estimate the Xo value; but, the best solution is to procure effective Weibull Analysis Software.

Chapter Footnotes:

Mechanical Reliability by A D S Carter, B Sc. C Eng., John Wiley & Sons, 1972

The Use of Weibull in Defect Data Analysis, Warwick Manufacturing Group, 6 Dec 2004
https://warwick.ac.uk

Chapter 10 Homework:

Japanese tea production (tons/hectare) is listed below for 56 years.

A. Create a 2 parameter Weibull Plot. Are data-points "arced"? Turn in plot and answer.

B. From Question A above, examine the plot and guess the value of Xo.

C. Use spreadsheet method to determine Beta, Eta and Xo for a 3 parameter Weibull Analysis. Turn in 3 Parameter Weibull plot and determined values for Beta, Eta and Xo.

1	15067	21	16672	41	18068		
2	15214	22	16770	42	18162		
3	15243	23	16770	43	18182		
4	15368	24	16795	44	18566		
5	15548	25	16836	45	18608		
6	15759	26	16865	46	18661		
7	15774	27	16966	47	18678		
8	15835	28	17097	48	18715		
9	15961	29	17136	49	18750		
10	15971	30	17173	50	18928		
11	16077	31	17243	51	19340		
12	16099	32	17370	52	19378		
13	16145	33	17456	53	19523		
14	16148	34	17548	54	20104		
15	16243	35	17606	55	20509		
16	16308	36	17658	56	20534		
17	16333	37	17679				
18	16339	38	17771				
19	16535	39	17812				
20	16579	40	18033				

Note: Japanese tea production data is from United Nations agricultural services. See credits for further information and release information.

Chapter 11: Computer Programs & Weibull Analysis

Weibull Software can only be evaluated based on its ability to help analysts achieve typical goals of performing Weibull Analysis. Chapter 11 explains how dedicated Weibull software can help and also identifies some of the extra capabilities that are often included.

This chapter is not intended to be a commercial endorsement of any product; yet, the considerable effort required to explore a software package restricts the number of applications discussed. We will examine Weibull-DR in some detail, Watson-Weibull in a cursory manner and compare those to spreadsheet based Weibull analysis. Identification and summary presentation of known Weibull Analysis programs and capabilities is provided by Tables 11-1 and 11-2.

There are four primary goals for Weibull Analysis:

- Characterization of an underlying population represented by a data-set as either a two or a three parameter Weibull Distribution. This is usually achieved by Weibull Plot, in order to determine Weibull parameters Beta, Eta and for the 3 parameter, Xo.

- Description of population percentages within specified ranges of the x value.

- Prediction of probability of occurrence for future events.

- Determination of test duration required to demonstrate compliance to a life requirement.

There are many secondary goals including:

- Failure characterization for a complex machine with multiple failure modes.

- Comparison of Weibull to other distributions for describing a data-set.

- Computation of reliability metrics corresponding to a Weibull distribution.

- Numerous special purpose analyses such as bearing life.

Advantages of Dedicated Weibull Software:

<u>Weibull software</u> typically provides superior user interface, well integrated and tested equations and clear results display. Dedicated Weibull software provides the only really effective 3 parameter Weibull analysis approach. Many Weibull packages provide special purpose modules that address various circumstances, types of components and produce reports. These benefits are best compared to the likely alternative - spreadsheets.

<u>Spreadsheets</u>: General purpose spreadsheets can be used for many 2 parameter Weibull analysis tasks; but, have the following limitations:

- Three parameter Weibull Analysis by spreadsheet is not practical.

- Infrequent Weibull use makes inter-column equation definition error prone.

- Spreadsheet preparation of suitable analysis records requires tedious effort and often yields inconsistent records.

- Determination of Reliability Metrics (e.g. MTBF) requires custom development.

Well designed Weibull analysis software overcomes most of these issues and is thus far superior to spreadsheets. Use of spreadsheets throughout this book was a teaching decision, rather than a technical one.

Weibull-DR Capabilities:

Weibull-DR is a mature program with an intuitive command structure embedded in single screen displays that are themselves mini-reports. Accuracy of Weibull-DR for both 2 and 3 parameter Weibull data-set characterization was verified. The design philosophy of Weibull-DR is stated by the user manual, "… other programs have become more complex and difficult to learn and work with, than is justified. We trust our efforts here will help remedy this situation." My experience with Weibull-DR confirms ease of use.

Upon program start-up, the user encounters a small, high level menu (below left) and a large data-entry screen (below right) which incorporates the most often needed commands in a left edge column of buttons.

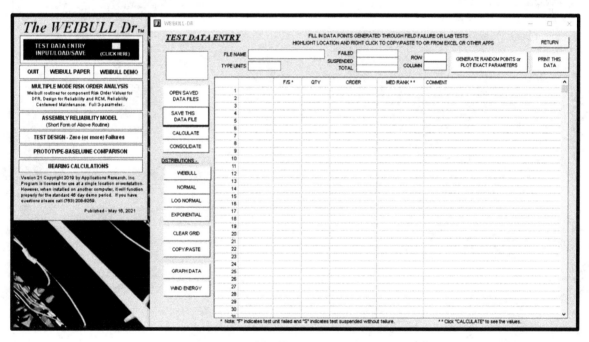

Figure 11-1: Weibull-DR Startup Screen (1)

Specialized analyses may be selected from the smaller menu to the far left; but most sessions will proceed with data entry in tabular entry screen at the right. After entering File Name, and units (hours, cycles, minutes, meters , etc.), data points 1 through "N" are entered in the "spreadsheet like" grid. The most common data entry situation is entry of failure times

203

corresponding to single failure events (e.g. 2300 cycles, failure of bolt, quantity 1). If 2 or more events should occur at the same measured x value (e.g. Both failed at 2.3 hours), the number of events is entered in the "QTY" column. For engineering tests, failed specimens are coded "F" and specimens removed due to instrumentation issues are coded "S" in the "F/S*" column. For natural phenomena all data points are normally coded "F" .

Weibull-DR Data Analysis:

Figure 11-2 below illustrates daily milk cow production (gallons per day) entered in the data-screen. Weibull-DR is currently capable of entering and analyzing 4000 data-points.

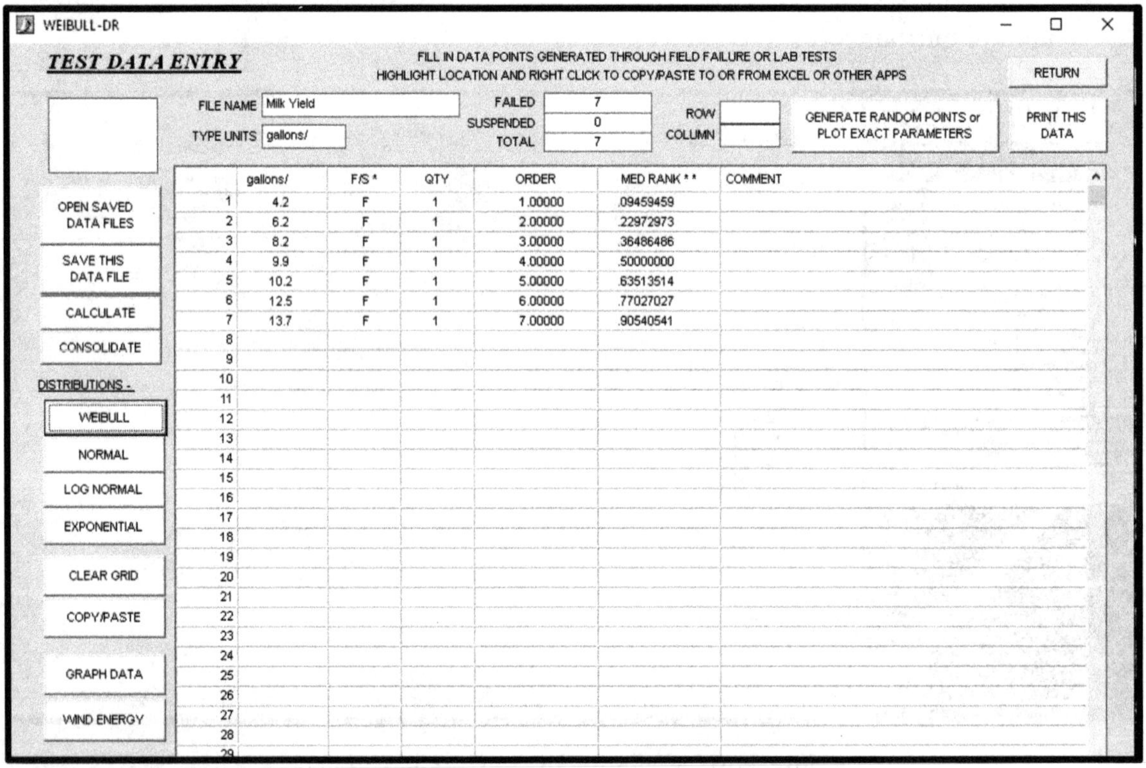

Figure 11-2: Daily Milk Production for 7 dairy cows

The Command Button column at left of data entry screen enables "single click" analysis of entered data. While Figure 11-3 shows results from "clicking" the WEIBULL command button, alternative statistical distributions may be applied according to button choice.

204

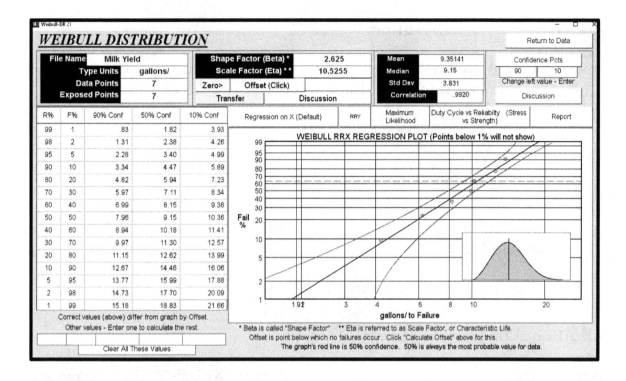

Figure 11-3: Daily Milk Production Weibull Plot

Figure 11-3 above displays the following analysis results:

- Weibull Parameters: β=2.625 and η=10.5255 at top center.

- Coefficient of Correlation = .9920 at top right (similar to R^2)

- Weibull Plot of data points along with best fit line and confidence bounds.

- A tabular presentation of upper and lower confidence bounds at left side table.

If a 3 parameter Weibull Analysis is desired, the "Offset (Click)" button (top center) is pressed to instantly reformulate the entire display accordingly. Converting back and forth is both easy and useful.

205

Analysis Report Generation:

A one page printed report can be generated with a single button "click" near top right of the screen. A consistent format is created which includes:

- Population description (Beta, Eta and Xo)

- PDF graph

- Weibull Plot

- Confidence bounds table

- Various Reliability inferred statistics

Additional Feature Summary:

Data analysis features of Weibull-DR have been summarized. Weibull-DR also includes many additional capabilities as part of the standard software package.

- Analysis of data-sets using normal, log-normal or exponential distributions.

- Analysis of the multi-mode failure distribution for complex machines.

- Means of reconciling wear-out analysis with end user usage spectrum.

- Determination of test duration for zero failure tests to achieve statistical significance.

- Special purpose modules for wind turbine power and for bearing life.

- A module to create Weibull data enabling Monte Carlo simulation.

- A data visualization module (for creation of data histograms)

- A Weibull equation visualization tool. (i.e. input Beta & Eta to see the result)

- Automatic creation of equivalent Reliability metrics (e.g. MTBF etc.)

- An efficient and well written 28 page manual.

- User support

As part of an independent Weibull-DR review, core analysis accuracy (β, η and Xo) has been validated for both 2 and 3 parameter Weibull distributions. Accurate Gaussian parameter determination for a data-set was also validated.

Watson-Weibull Program Capabilities:

The Watson-Weibull program is currently under development and its intended use is Weibull education and methods exploration. The program enables analysis by a variety of methods in comparison to Weibull-DR which uses the most accepted industry practices in a streamlined menu. Test cases run with both programs confirmed accuracy of Weibull-DR and significant accuracy improvement did not result from alternative methods.

Most of the Watson-Weibull analysis options are controlled by the Analysis Options GUI interface shown by Figure 11-4 below. While many of the options are also available in Weibull-DR, some of the more unusual options are summarized below.

- Failure Rank computations methods include modified Leonard Jones vs. Watson's Weibull Rank Adjustment (see page 162). Users may also choose analysis without discards.

- Alternative computation of Median Percent for data-points by the Benard Equation vs. the exact Linear Conjecture Equation.

- As with Weibull-DR, the user may select a variety of confidence bounds as desired.

- As with Weibull-DR, data may be analyzed as y fitted to x points or vice versa.

- Weibull-DR offers Maximum Probability Method, while Watson-Weibull does not.

Figure 11-4: Watson-Weibull Analysis Options

Once configured; the "Do It" button produces a Weibull Plot like Figure 11-5. The Weibull plot presents both traditional x, y axes, but also presents alternative axes with raw Weibull Y values and Natural Log values of the x variable (i.e. pseudo variables). It is hoped students can benefit from side from side axis presentation.

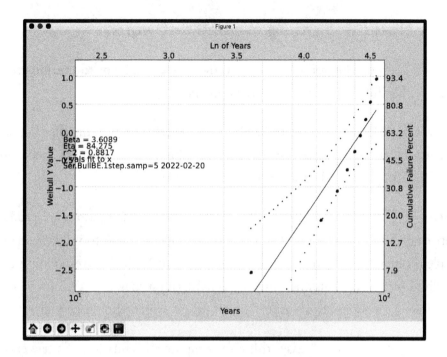

Figure 11-5: Watson-Weibull Plot

The Weibull Plot displays the following features:

- At the top left of the Weibull Plot, determined Weibull parameters and a coded description of chosen analysis options is presented.

- X and Y axes are presented as both pseudo and real axes.

- Confidence bounds are plotted above and below the fitted Weibull line.

- While Weibull-DR features a combined display and command screen, the Watson Weibull program has separate screens for each function.

Cautionary Notes Regarding Weibull Software:

It is inadvisable to rely on the outputs of an unproven product. Prior to routine use of a software package, the following checks are recommended:

- Accuracy of reducing data-set to Weibull (or other) statistical distribution should be validated using one or more test data sets with known answers. This book provides several carefully analyzed data sets that can be used.

- If Reliability Metrics correlated to Weibull (or other) distributions are produced, an effort to understand how the Weibull Program operates and to validate one or more sample problems is recommended. For example, an MTBF corresponding to a Weibull Distribution is a fixed number only if Beta=1. An estimated MTBF for values of Beta other than 1 thus implies additional assumptions which should be understood.

- Confidence bounds are a "fussy" thing to compute. If validation of a few examples is not feasible, reasonableness checks of general behavior should be performed. (See Charles Zaiontz PhD, Real Statistics Using Excel for discussion of confidence bounds)

- Prior to widespread use, Zero Failure test duration should be validated using a scientific calculator and Weibull Equations. See The New Weibull Handbook by Dr. Abernethy page 6-1 for details.

- Software making future risk predictions should be validated using examples from Chapter 8 of this book. Alternatively, Chapter 8 equations enable validation of computer software determinations by scientific calculator.

- Menu structures and technical focus vary greatly between products. A free use period should be requested to verify a particular product is suitable for the intended users.

Capability & Availability Matrices:

	Spreadsheet	Weibull-DR	Watson-Weibull
Weibull Plot	Yes	Yes	Yes
Determines β, η	Yes	Yes	Yes
Determines β, η, Xo	No	Yes	No
Confidence Bounds	No	Yes	Yes
Future Predictions	No	No	No
Test Duration	No	Yes	No
MultiMode Analysis	No	Yes	No
Gauss Distribution	No	Yes	No
R&M Metrics	No	Yes	Not Yet
Special Analyses	No	Yes	No
Educational Content	No	Yes	Yes
Tailorable Analysis	No	No	Yes
User Programming	Yes	No	No
User Support	No	Yes	No
Commercial Cost	No	Yes	Not Yet

Table 11-1: Product Capability Summary

	Website	Demo?
Reliance Weibull	https://relyence.com	Yes
SuperSMITH Weibull	www.weibullnews.com	Yes
Weibull-WorkBench	www.isograph.com	Yes
Watson-Weibull	www.dionysus.biz	TBD
Weibull-DR	www.applicationsresearch.com	Yes
Weibull++	www.reliasoft.com	?
MiniTab	www.minitab.com	Yes

Table 11-2: Known Weibull Software

Chapter 11 Conclusions:

While spreadsheets provide an excellent way of exploring Weibull methods, dedicated Weibull software is recommended. The primary benefit of such software is convenient/efficient analysis of data for the 3 parameter Weibull equation.

Commercial Weibull software provides many useful capabilities beyond data correlation to Weibull Distributions. When the range of available analyses is considered, the cost of good quality Weibull software is easily justified.

Certain cautions should be applied when selecting and before trusting Weibull software.

- The free use period should be used to verify accuracy of solutions and convenience.

- Documentation of proposed products should be evaluated. The two evaluation criteria are a) Will documentation help a new user accomplish an analysis? b) Are technical details regarding analysis methods sufficient to answer the more obvious technical questions?

- Compatibility of Weibull Software with intended target platforms should be verified before purchase. If installation problems occur, willingness of the Supplier to provide help is an indication of their commitment to user support.

- During the free use period, sample problems with known answers should be used to test the proposed software for accuracy. Reviewers should expect a small error for the location parameter (Xo) of the 3 parameter Weibull because it is solved by trial and error.

- User convenience should be considered during the evaluation period. A very complex program is difficult to use on an occasional basis and intermittent use is likely.

- Menus and reports vary between products. Some products fit nicely into an R&M organization, while others fit well into more design oriented organizations.

Acknowledgement:

While writing this book, Applications Research, Inc., provided me an extended use license which made detailed review of their product possible. The Weibull-DR menu structures were intuitive and convenient. Weibull data-set characterization was accurate. The user manual was compact but reasonably thorough. The staff at Applications Research was experienced and helpful. Time constraints and software availability prevented similar evaluation of other products, but many are available in the market place and most offer a free evaluation period.

I thank John Berner of Applications Research for providing his product for evaluation.

Chapter Footnotes:

1. Authorization to display Weibull-DR screens as shown were extended by e-mail. John Berner email of 9 March 2022.

Chapter 12: Weibull Analysis in Retrospect

The Weibull distribution is but one of many probability distributions that are used to describe real world data. Other well known distributions include the Gaussian, the Binomial and the Log-Normal; but, Weibull is unique in two respects:

- It is amazingly versatile in its ability to model real world data.

- Weibull analysis procedures are unusually clear cut and efficient.

These characteristics make it the ideal complement to the Gaussian.

The core method presented in The Weibull Bible is the Weibull Plot. There is also the competing Maximum Likelihood Method (MLM) for correlating data-sets to a Weibull Equation. While some analysts prefer the MLM method, most engineers and many scientists prefer the Weibull Plot method. Strengths of the Weibull Plot method are:

- An easily understood basis for correlating the 2 parameter Weibull to a data-set.

- Visual representation of data-point issues including "end point data drupe," and the relationship between data-points and confidence bounds.

Put simply, many of us prefer the Weibull Plot method because we understand it at a visceral level.

The mathematics of Weibull is apolitical. Many Weibull problems can be solved by spreadsheet, but data ultimately behaves as it will. Dedicated Weibull software extends practical Weibull implementation to include the three parameter Weibull equation when demanded by the data. During engineering development, a single use of 3 parameter Weibull modeling can save a design and avoid millions of dollars in redesign cost. The 3 parameter Weibull can likewise make critical contributions to scientific efforts. While spreadsheets provide a good learning experience, the serious user is encouraged to investigate dedicated Weibull software.

Weibull analysis can be applied to a wide range of endeavor. There are numerous developers of Weibull software, each with a unique perspective. The result is a range of products, which typically includes special modules that address particular needs. The Weibull-DR's inclusion of a module adapted for wind generation that elegantly analyzes power output from characterized wind is one example. (note: The wind analysis module was created at customer request.) While three parameter Weibull Analysis is sufficient reason to invest in Weibull software, special purpose software "add-ons" may provide substantial advantages for your circumstance.

This book discussed "data-point mischief" in detail. It is important to realize the issue is not unique to Weibull, but affects all statistical characterizations. Despite the cautions voiced, Weibull analysis offers scientists and engineers a powerful tool to aid their understanding of diverse phenomena. In conclusion, Weibull is just one more weapon in an arsenal of statistical tools; but Weibull is a very powerful one.

Comments and suggestions are welcome. Please address to:

Paul F. Watson

PO Box 102

Oceanside OR 97134

Page Intentionally Left Blank

Appendix A: Tables of Median Percent

DataCnt	Number of Data Points ---->																	
	3	4	5	6	7	8	9	10	11	12	13	14	15	16	17	18	19	20
1	0.2063	0.1591	0.1294	0.1091	0.0943	0.0830	0.0741	0.0670	0.0611	0.0561	0.0519	0.0483	0.0452	0.0424	0.0400	0.0378	0.0358	0.0341
2	0.5000	0.3864	0.3147	0.2655	0.2295	0.2021	0.1806	0.1632	0.1489	0.1368	0.1266	0.1178	0.1101	0.1034	0.0975	0.0922	0.0874	0.0831
3	0.7937	0.6136	0.5000	0.4218	0.3648	0.3213	0.2871	0.2594	0.2366	0.2175	0.2013	0.1873	0.1751	0.1644	0.1550	0.1465	0.1390	0.1322
4		0.8409	0.6853	0.5782	0.5000	0.4404	0.3935	0.3557	0.3244	0.2982	0.2760	0.2568	0.2401	0.2254	0.2125	0.2009	0.1905	0.1812
5			0.8706	0.7345	0.6352	0.5596	0.5000	0.4519	0.4122	0.3789	0.3506	0.3263	0.3051	0.2865	0.2700	0.2553	0.2421	0.2302
6				0.8909	0.7705	0.6787	0.6065	0.5481	0.5000	0.4596	0.4253	0.3958	0.3700	0.3475	0.3275	0.3097	0.2937	0.2793
7					0.9057	0.7979	0.7129	0.6443	0.5878	0.5404	0.5000	0.4653	0.4350	0.4085	0.3850	0.3641	0.3453	0.3283
8						0.9170	0.8194	0.7406	0.6756	0.6211	0.5747	0.5347	0.5000	0.4695	0.4425	0.4184	0.3968	0.3774
9							0.9259	0.8368	0.7634	0.7018	0.6494	0.6042	0.5650	0.5305	0.5000	0.4728	0.4484	0.4264
10								0.9330	0.8511	0.7825	0.7240	0.6737	0.6300	0.5915	0.5575	0.5272	0.5000	0.4755
11									0.9389	0.8632	0.7987	0.7432	0.6949	0.6525	0.6150	0.5816	0.5516	0.5245
12										0.9439	0.8734	0.8127	0.7599	0.7135	0.6725	0.6359	0.6032	0.5736
13											0.9481	0.8822	0.8249	0.7746	0.7300	0.6903	0.6547	0.6226
14												0.9517	0.8899	0.8356	0.7875	0.7447	0.7063	0.6717
15													0.9548	0.8966	0.8450	0.7991	0.7579	0.7207
16														0.9576	0.9025	0.8535	0.8095	0.7698
17															0.9600	0.9078	0.8610	0.8188
18																0.9622	0.9126	0.8678
19																	0.9642	0.9169
20																		0.9659

Appendix B: Weibull Plot Analysis Tables

Watson Standard Template (Data Without Discards)

See following page for data-sets with Discards

Ignore 'Blank' Columns

Responsible: _____

Watson Standard Template

Test Description: _____

Record Total Number of Samples N: _____

Test Date: _____

Order	ContraOrder	DataValue	Discard	Rank	AdjRank	Median%
1	Blank		Blank		Blank	
2	Blank		Blank		Blank	
3	Blank		Blank		Blank	
4	Blank		Blank		Blank	
5	Blank		Blank		Blank	
6	Blank		Blank		Blank	
7	Blank		Blank		Blank	
8	Blank		Blank		Blank	
9	Blank		Blank		Blank	
10	Blank		Blank		Blank	
11	Blank		Blank		Blank	
12	Blank		Blank		Blank	
13	Blank		Blank		Blank	
14	Blank		Blank		Blank	
15	Blank		Blank		Blank	
16	Blank		Blank		Blank	
17	Blank		Blank		Blank	
18	Blank		Blank		Blank	
19	Blank		Blank		Blank	
20	Blank		Blank		Blank	
21	Blank		Blank		Blank	
22	Blank		Blank		Blank	
23	Blank		Blank		Blank	
24	Blank		Blank		Blank	
25	Blank		Blank		Blank	

Appendix B: Weibull Plot Analysis Tables

Watson Standard Template - Data with Discards

See previous page for data-sets without Discards

Ignore 'Blank' columns.

Responsible: _____

Watson Standard Template

Test Description: _____

Record Total Number of Samples N: _____

Test Date: _____

Order	ContraOrder	DataValue	Discard	Rank	AdjRank	Median%
1				Blank		
2				Blank		
3				Blank		
4				Blank		
5				Blank		
6				Blank		
7				Blank		
8				Blank		
9				Blank		
10				Blank		
11				Blank		
12				Blank		
13				Blank		
14				Blank		
15				Blank		
16				Blank		
17				Blank		
18				Blank		
19				Blank		
20				Blank		
21				Blank		
22				Blank		
23				Blank		
24				Blank		
25				Blank		

Page Intentionally Left Blank

Appendix C: Review of PDF and CDF Concepts

Introduction:

While most people intuitively understand a histogram, the concept of a Probability Density Function seems abstract. Appendix C will do two things.

- It will give a good review of histograms.

- It will explain that a PDF is an evolved histogram. Appendix C begins with an example histogram, and converts it in 4 steps to a PDF. Thus, the PDF can be understood in terms of its histogram origins.

Histograms:

The meaning of a histogram is intuitive, yet most people confronted with "building one" struggle over practical questions:

- "How many bars should I use?"

- "Is it bad to use too many bars? What happens if I do?"

- "Is the y axis supposed to be count, percent or what?"

A histogram is that commonly used graphic presenting the number of observed values corresponding to "bucket ranges" of the x variable (see Figure C-1 below). For example, a college dean might want to understand how various professors are ranking their students. The grade histogram for Dr. Jones follows:

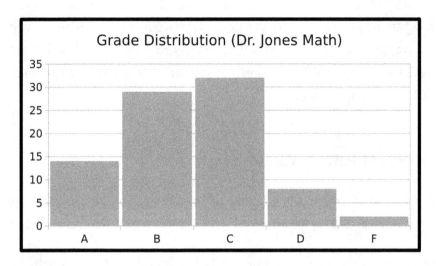

Figure C-1: Histogram of Dr. Jones Grades

The Histogram above provides an easily understood visual which shows most of Dr. Jone's students passed and his grading system is a somewhat optimistic record of student achievement, with far more A's than F's. While it is intuitive to use 5 bars (one for each letter grade), we could equally well use 15 (A+, A, A-, B+, B ... etc.), or we could use some other, far less natural number of bars.

For the grade example, five bars seems natural; however, histograms can describe a variety of things, like forest tree size, Texas cotton yield per acre, rainfall variation in Tillamook or length of 'identical' bolts off an assembly line. None of these examples "suggests" an intuitively correct number of bars.

In general, there is no "correct/natural" way to construct a histogram but guidelines follow:

- The histogram should present information in a way that is easy to understand.

- The y axis should represent the count of students, count of trees of various sizes etc.

- The x axis should identify "range buckets" corresponding to each of the bars. In general, the "range buckets" should be the same size for all bars (e.g. don't group F and D grades into the same bar, while A, B and C are each treated as separate bars).

- Too few bars results in a course and uninformative histogram. Too many bars is informative, but results in an unrealistically 'jagged' histogram. For 500 samples, perhaps 9 to 15 bars may be appropriate. Smaller sample counts require fewer bars to avoid a "jagged" appearance.

Histogram Presentation Variations:

Insight can be obtained by creating two histograms, with 4 bars vs. 9 bars each representing the same data. By comparing results, we can learn what happens as we increase the bar count.

To make these comparisons, a collection of 500 data points was created by substituting random numbers into a Weibull equation. The effect is much like walking through a forest and recording a random selection of 500 tree girths. While the data-set could represent anything, the dialog that follows assumes it represents the girth of trees in Oregon.

Figure C-2 was constructed with 4 bars to represent tree girth. The "bucket ranges" are all 9.38 meters wide. The most common size for a tree is between 9.38 meters and 18.75 meters.

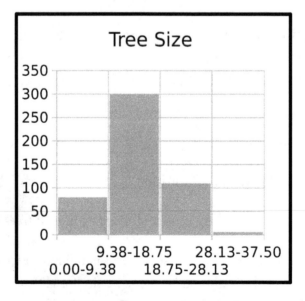

Figure C-2: Tree Girth in Meters (4 bar histogram)

The choice of 4 bars was completely arbitrary. The underlying data-set of 500 values could just as easily be divided into 9 bars (hence 4.17 meters wide) with the following equally valid result:

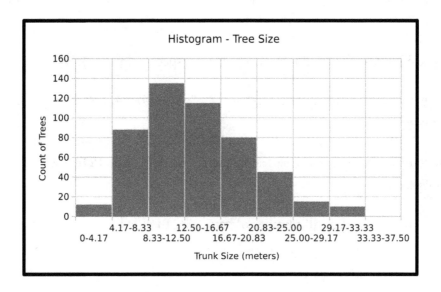

Figure C-3: Tree Girth in Meters (9 bar histogram)

Examining Figure C-3, it is evident that increasing the bar count to 9 provides more detailed information. We now see that about 10 meters was the most common size. The 9 bar histogram shows an orderly transition pattern from one bar to the next. This is good because underlying populations usually exhibit smooth transitions over the full range of x.

Despite the good results with 9 bars, there is nothing "natural" about 9 bars, and we would be equally justified in using 19 or 25 or any other number of bars. If a 19 bar histogram is created with the same data-set, the graph becomes "ragged looking" with some of the bars near the ends missing. This results from stretching too little data over too many bars.

For the sample tree data, an informative and nice looking histogram results from using 9 to 12 bars as illustrated by Figure C-3.

Histograms and PDF Graphs:

Quoting www.weibull.com, "The Probability Density Function (PDF) ... is a continuous representation of a histogram that shows how the ... (observed variable) is distributed ... along the 'x' domain."

Histograms and PDF Graphs are different in several respects.

- Histograms show quantity of items for each "bucket range". PDFs represents percent as area under a curve.

- Histograms, show x axis as a series of "range buckets". The PDF x axis is a continuous number line.

- The histogram has a small number of bars. The PDF is based on an infinite number of bars.

In the section that follows, we will convert Tree Histogram Figure C-3 into an equivalent PDF in four steps. The four steps correspond to Graphs A though D of Figure C-4.

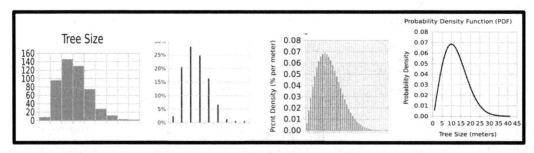

Figure C-4: Evolution of Histogram to PDF

Graph A: Start with Figure C-4 "Tree Size". Convert y axis value for each bar to percent. e.g. using values from 2nd bar of Figure C-3 we have 98 trees divided by 500 samples = 19.6%.

Graph B: Convert "x" axis "range buckets" to center point decimal numbers and "y" to density numbers. See three bullets below. Based on Figure C-3 2nd bar, we compute as follows:

- Convert x from "range buckets" to center point values: (4.17+8.33)/2 = 6.25

- Change bar height to density. 19.6% divided by (8.33-4.17) = 4.7 percent/meter

- Check: 4.17 meter wide x 4.7% per meter= 19.6% Bar still represents 19.6%. Excellent!

Graph C: Increase the number of samples to near infinity (Figure C4 3rd graph). This step is a bit "creative" because our sample size is only 500 trees. Some "fancy math" is required to estimate each bar height for a huge number of bars.

Graph D: Replace the "bars" with a smooth curve across the bar tops to create PDF at right of C-4. When we finally reach the PDF (far right graph in Figure C-4), bars no longer exist and bar height has no meaning. It is the area under the curved line that has physical meaning. In fact, the area between x=0 and x=15 meters is precisely the percentage of trees having a girth less than 15 meters! Any PDF can be interpreted in the same manner.

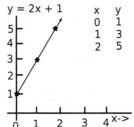

Why Do Statisticians Like PDFs?

As a visual presentation, the histogram is very good; but, the math of statistics does not work with pictures. Algebra students are familiar with equations that represent graphs and vice versa.

In a like manner, a PDF image can be reduced to an equation using methods presented in this book. The equation form of a PDF is preferred because it supports math needed for Weibull Analysis.

Comments about the Probability Density Function:

The Probability Density Function (PDF) is an odd sort of graph. It is odd in the respect that y values of the plot have little meaning; rather, the area under the curve has meaning. Readers familiar with analysis using the Standard Normal Distribution (Gaussian) have seen similar curves where area represents percent.

Optional: "What is the y axis really?", you may ask. When I drive my car, the speedometer has little meaning; because, the real meaning is the miles that "whiz by" with passing of time. PDF Y axis values are much the same. They indicate how fast percent is accumulating as we move to larger and larger x values. Calculus concepts give it clear meaning. The Y axis value at a given x location is the derivative of Percent Area with respect to x.

A Historical Example- the PDF and the CDF:

The concepts of the Probability Density Function (PDF) and the Cumulative Density Function (CDF) will be explained using a historical example. While the example is historical, details were fabricated.

During the 1880's, a French scientist studied Bubonic Plague outbreaks in India. Based on field observations, he made the following conclusions (ε):

- Plague is probably spread by fleas carried by rats.

- Plague explodes into an epidemic when infected fleas per hundred approaches 2.

- Infected fleas per hundred never exceeds 3. This only occurs in severe epidemics.

The Frenchman was a skilled mathematician, so he constructed a simple PDF that characterized the percent of villages corresponding to various infected flea counts. His PDF follows:

Graphic Comparison of PDF and CDF:

Below, we present the Bubonic Plague PDF and its corresponding CDF.

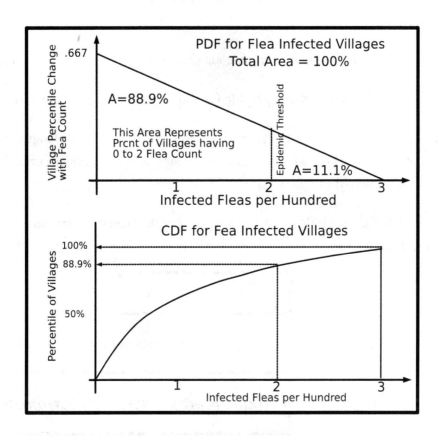

Figure C-5: Illustration of PDF vs. CDF Relationship

Please observe that the PDF area for the x region from x=0 to x=2 is 88.9%. Examining the CDF, we find for x=2, the "y" value is 88.9%. Thus CDF y reflects PDF area from x=0.

Definition of CDF Curve: The CDF curve may be defined as follows. For every PDF value "xi", the corresponding CDF "y" value is exactly the PDF area for the region from "x"=0 to "x"=xi. It is worth reading and re-reading the definition while studying Figure C-5 above until the meaning is internalized.

Mathematical Definitions of PDF and CDF Curves:

The ideas shown above graphically, can be reduced to mathematical expression. In general, the graphic representations are a bit more intuitive while the equation form of PDFs and CDFs produce precise answers.

- A PDF can be defined by either a graphic (as shown above) or by an equation.

- A CDF can be defined by either a graphic (as shown above) or by an equation.

Previously discussed rules continue to apply, but need to be expressed in the language of equations. The mathematics which addresses rates of change, and areas under curves is Calculus which is implemented as follows:

The Area under a PDF Curve = 100%: The corresponding mathematical statement applies to all PDF functions. Thus Eq C1:

Eq C1
$$\int_0^{max} f(x)dx = 100\,\%$$

The Area under a PDF Curve from "x"=a to "x=b" can be computed from Eq C2 below:

Eq C2
$$\int_a^b f(x)dx = areaunderthecurvefromatob$$

And finally, the CDF equation can be mathematically generated from the PDF equation by:

Eq C3
$$CDF:F(x) = \int PDF(x)dx$$

Discussion:

- The above equation states that the CDF "y" value corresponding to any PDF value "x" can be found mathematically. Furthermore, if the PDF equation is known, calculus integration will generate an equation that defines the entire set of "y" values for the

CDF equation (i.e. creates an equation that will compute the total area from x=0 to x=a based on the original PDF equation for any value of x.)

- While the CDF can (in principle) be created by integrating the PDF equation, the math sometimes surpasses our ability. Calculus students typically learn how to integrate 20 or 30 equation forms; but, there are many equations no one has ever integrated.

Math and the Bubonic Plague Example (Math Descriptions)

The PDF graph Figure C5 PDF is obviously a linear equation. For the domain 0<x<3, Eq C4 equation below defines the PDF. The CDF is computed by Equations C5 and C6 below.

Eq C4: $f(x) = -.2222 * x + .667$ for $0 < x < 3$

Eq C5: $$F(x) = \int (-.2222x + .6667)dx$$

Eq C6: $$CDF: F(x) = -.1111 \cdot x^2 + .6667 \cdot x$$

Appendix C Summary:

- Both PDF and CDF represent the Percentile (cumulative percent) of the population of objects having some property below value represented on the "x" axis.

- Both PDF and CDF can be represented by graphs.

- The area under the PDF curve represents Percentile.

- The "y" axis value of any point on the CDF curve represents the percentile value that corresponds to the x axis value.

231

- Both PDF and CDF can be represented by equations.

- The integral from x=0 to x=a of the PDF curve is cumulative percent of the population (Percentile) having values below a.

- The integral from x=b to x=c of the PDF curve is the percentage of the parent population having values between b and c.

- The "y" value calculated by the CDF equation substituting some value a in place of x is percent of the population having a measured property less than a.

- The CDF equation can be computed by performing the calculus integral of the PDF equation (provided it is possible to perform the math). If the CDF equation is known, it is likewise possible to calculate the PDF equation by use of calculus.

Appendix Notes:

(ε) Source of Inspiration: Black Death at the Golden Gate by David K. Randall (c) 2019 W.W. Norton & Company

Appendix D: Binomial Equation & Median Percent Calculation

Introduction:

Performance of Weibull Analysis requires determination of Median Percents corresponding to each data-point in a data-set. At present, the only method for computing Median Percents that rests firmly on theory, is the binomial probability model and its binomial equation.

The binomial equation enables probability computation for a specified number of successes out of N attempts. In plain English, if the probability of brewing a bad batch of beer is 3%, then the probability of brewing 4 bad batches out of 10 can be computed (provided success of one batch is independent of the other batches.)

- Appendix D presents theory and provides examples of using the Binomial Equation.

- Appendix D demonstrates use of the binomial to determine Median Percents for data-sets.

- Appendix D presents means of validating Median Percent predictions of the Linear Conjecture

Background Discussion:

The binomial equation is the mathematical expression of the binomial distribution. If we consider the simultaneous occurrence of five independent binary events (hit vs. doesn't hit), each term of the equation corresponds to the probability of a possible outcome. To avoid ambiguity, I present the following example.

A WWI battleship simultaneously fired a group (salvo) of five cannon shells. Historically, the long term hit percentage was 5%. There were six possible outcomes from a salvo.

5 hits and 0 misses, 4 hits and 1 miss, 3 hits and 2 misses

2 hits and 3 misses, 1 hit and 4 misses, 0 hits and 5 misses

We refer to probability of success as p which equals .05 as stated above. We refer to the probability of failures q (misses) which equals 100%-5% = .95

The universe of possible outcomes is described by the six terms below, each of which numerically predicts the probability of a particular outcome. Note: For Equation D1, the 5th term involving p1 and q4 is associated with probability of 1 success and 4 failures. Other terms may be similarly interpreted.

Eq D-1:
$$\boxed{1p^5q^0 + 5p^4q^1 + 10p^3q^2 + 10p^2q^3 + 5p^1q^4 + 1p^0q^5}$$

Eq D-2:
$$\boxed{5p^1q^4 = 5 \cdot .05^1 \cdot .95^4 = 20\%}$$

Example Calculation: The 5th term calculates the probability of 1 hit and 4 misses:

The probability of 1 hit and 4 misses is 20% as computed by Equation D-2. Equation D-1 above states that the sum of probability for all the various outcomes is 100%.

Binomial Equation D1 above conforms exactly to the laws of probability. The seemingly arbitrary coefficients correspond to the number of different ways a particular outcome can happen. For example: 1 success and 4 failures can occur in exactly 5 ways (the 1st could hit, 2nd could hit ... the 5th could hit).

The binomial equation always has one more term than the number of events described. The particular sequence of number coefficients (1 5 10 10 5 1) is different for 5 cannon shells vs. 6

234

cannon shells vs. 7 cannon shells etc. Thus for each data-set size, there is a required sequence of number coefficients which can be determined by Combination Theory. (see Note 1 at end of Appendix D)

Determination of Median Percent:

Concept development is needed to support determination of Median Percents. Explanation will be provided assuming a five point data-set (that has been sorted from small to large).

1. For a 5 point data-set, there exist 5 Median Percents, each corresponding to a data-point. Thus, there is a 1st Median Percent, a 2nd Median Percent ... and a 5th Median Percent.

2. Data-points are evidence about some underlying population. If we consider a data-set of 5 points, there exists some percentage of the population that "traps" just enough to be 50% likely to contain the 5th data-point. That percentage is called the 5th Median Percent and is represented by area p% in the figure below. There are similar but smaller areas corresponding to the 1st, 2nd, 3rd and 4th data-points.

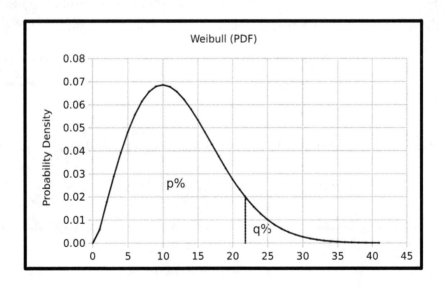

Figure D-1: PDF showing Median Percent Area

PDF Figure D-1 is assumed to describe a population represented by the data-points, and is key to understanding binomial equation calculation of Median Percents. When 5 data-points are collected (and sorted), each one that falls into area p% (under consideration) is a "binomial success" (each one falling into zone q% is a binomial failure).

3. Shift Focus to 1st point. To compute Median Percent for data-point 1, we want to determine area p such that it is 50% likely that the first data-point will be within the region. There are five circumstances where the 1st data-point x value will be in region p as listed below.

- Exactly one data-point falls in region p (computed from 1st Term of Binomial)

- Two data-points fall in region p (computed from 2nd Term)

- Three data-points fall in region p (computed from 3rd Term)

- four data-points fall in region p (computed from 4th Term)

- All five data-points fall in region p (computed from 5th Term)

The probability of 1st data-point being so located, is thus the sum of probabilities of all five circumstances. To find the value of p, we add up the 1st through 5th probability terms of Eq D1 and set them equal to .50. We then evaluate the equation to find the value of p.

Eq D-3:
$$\boxed{1p^5q^0 + 5p^4q^1 + 10p^3q^2 + 10p^2q^3 + 5p^1q^4 = .50}$$

There are two difficulties in solving Eq D3 for the value of p.

- The equation has 2 variables. This is easily overcome by substituting 1-p in place of q

- The resulting 5th power equation cannot be solved by algebra.

The usual way of solving Eq D3 is by trial and error substitution. We simply guess a value for p (then q=1-p), "plug" guess values of p and q into Eq D3 and see whether equality results. When it doesn't, we guess again and test the result. Repeated guesses can best be accomplished by spreadsheet as shown below (Row 15 is the approximate answer)

←Guess Values →		1st Term	2nd Term	3rd Term	4th Term	5th Term	
p	1-p	1p^5*q^0	5p^4*q^1	10p^3*q^2	10p^2*q*3	5p^1*q^4	Sums
0.01	0.99	0.000	0.000	0.000	0.001	0.048	0.049
0.02	0.98	0.000	0.000	0.000	0.004	0.092	0.096
0.03	0.97	0.000	0.000	0.000	0.008	0.133	0.141
0.04	0.96	0.000	0.000	0.001	0.014	0.170	0.185
0.05	0.95	0.000	0.000	0.001	0.021	0.204	0.226
0.06	0.94	0.000	0.000	0.002	0.030	0.234	0.266
0.07	0.93	0.000	0.000	0.003	0.039	0.262	0.304
0.08	0.92	0.000	0.000	0.004	0.050	0.287	0.341
0.09	0.91	0.000	0.000	0.006	0.061	0.309	0.376
0.10	0.90	0.000	0.000	0.008	0.073	0.328	0.410
0.11	0.89	0.000	0.001	0.011	0.085	0.345	0.442
0.12	0.88	0.000	0.001	0.013	0.098	0.360	0.472
0.13	0.87	0.000	0.001	0.017	0.111	0.372	0.502
0.14	0.86	0.000	0.002	0.020	0.125	0.383	0.530
0.15	0.85	0.000	0.002	0.024	0.138	0.392	0.556

Figure D-2: Example Trial & Error Solution

There are three uses for Equation D3:

- Direct determination of Median Percent for data-set of size N, by summing the correct terms. A trial and error solution similar to Figure D-2 is applied to enable guess validation until the correct Median Percent is found. This must be done for each of the data-points to produce N Median Percents.

- Optional: Use of some "magical method" may enable us to immediately predict the answer. This "magically determined" Median Percent could then be confirmed using Equation D-3. It so happens that we have such a method and it is called the Linear Conjecture. If predictions of the Linear Conjecture are substituted into Eq D-3 we should immediately confirm the prediction for that particular Median Percent and a great deal of tedious work is eliminated.

- Optional: It is worth observing that a computer loop which confirms the accuracy of medians corresponding to each data-point thus confirms the Linear Conjecture for the data-set size evaluated. If an outer loop ranging from 3 to 1000 were employed to establish the data-set size, then the Linear Conjecture could be shown correct for the realistic range of data-set sizes.

4. For five point data-sets, the terms needed for each of the five Median Percents are shown below, and the evident scheme can be applied to data-sets of any size. The logic has been explained above.

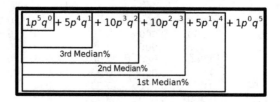

Figure D-3: Terms Needed for Each Median Percent (5 points)

5. The Binomial Median Percent Determination Equation can be codified as: Eq D4 where

- N = number of data-points in the data-set

- r = the data-point (1 to N) who's Median Percent we want.

- i = floating index indicating term from equation D3 (i.e. 1st term, 2nd term … etc.)

Eq D-4

$$\sum_{i=1}^{(N-r+1)} {_N}C_{(i-1)} \cdot p^{(N-i+1)} \cdot q^{(i-1)} = .50$$

Conclusion:

Use of the Binomial Equation to compute Median Percents for a data-set of size N has been explained and examples provided. The method demonstrated above is applicable only to integer numbered data points (1st, 2nd, 3rd … last) which is an inherent limitation of the Binomial Method. The method presented is sufficient to determine the Median Percents for a data-set of any size N.

The method presented also provides a basis for "brute force" validation of Median Percent determination by The Linear Conjecture. Such "brute force" demonstration is necessarily performed by computer iteration of data-set sizes from 3 to the maximum number realistically expected to occur. See Appendix E for Linear Conjecture justification.

Appendix D Notes: Combinatorial Computation

The number coefficients for a binomial expansion having 6 terms are shown by Equation D-5 below. For six terms, each term represents probability of a particular number of "successes" ranging from 5 to zero. For each term (1st through 6th), the number coefficient is equal to the number of ways that "success" can occur. While we shan't explain this in detail, it is usually computed by math combinatorials, and computation method is summarized below. It may also interest the reader, that if we were to compute $(p+q)^5$ using methods of algebra, we would end up creating exactly the same sequence of coefficients shown in Equation D-5 below. [try multiplying out $(x+y)^5$ and see what you get.]

1. Computation of Binomial Equation coefficients can be accomplished as follows:

Eq D-5 $$\boxed{1p^5q^0 + 5p^4q^1 + 10p^3q^2 + 10p^2q^3 + 5p^1q^4 + 1p^0q^5}$$

2. For 4th term of 5 data-points: We want to know out of five tries, how many ways 2 successes occur:

Coefficient = $_NC_{i-1}$

Coefficient for 4th Term: $_5C_{4-1}$ = 5! / [3! * (5-3)!] = 10

3. Two successes can happen in 10 different ways. The coefficient for term 4 is 10. This is consistent with probability theory where probability is increased according to the number of ways an event (or state) can occur.

The combinatorial method above correctly computes the 4th Binomial coefficient for a group of five events (this would correspond to five data-points). The full sequence for 1st through 6th term coefficients is: 1 5 10 10 5 1 and each term can be computed as shown above. The general method works equally well for data-sets of any number of data points.

End of Appendix D Discussion:

Appendix E: Justifying the Linear Conjecture

Introduction:

The reader is reminded of the need to compute Median Percents corresponding to data-points when performing Weibull analysis. The Linear Conjecture is a newly discovered method for conceptualizing and computing Median Percents for any data-point i, belonging to a data-set of size N. The method is codified in a closed form equation, which can accept both integer and non-integer data-point ordinal numbers (non integer ordinal numbers are sometimes called adjusted ranks and result from test samples prematurely removed from testing).

Traditional methods for computing a Median Percent corresponding to a data-point include:

- Closed form but approximate Benard Equation

- Tables of Median Percent (based on trial and error computer solution of the Binomial Equation)

- Direct application of the Binomial Equation which is impractical.

The much needed closed form solution is provided by The Linear Conjecture. Median Percents computed by The Linear Conjecture are precise.

History of Linear Conjecture: When I first studied Weibull Analysis methods, I was struck by the oddity of assigning five data points Median Percents as 12.94%, 31.38%, 50%, 68.62% and 86.06% in lieu of the expected 20%, 40% ... 100% corresponding to percent of failed samples. A Median Percent table like the one below, provided clear direction; yet, the mystery surrounding this strange methodology remained.

5 Data Points	
Ordinal Number	Median Percent
1	12.94%
2	31.38%
3	50.00%
4	68.62%
5	86.06%

Table E-1: Median Percents for 5 Data Points

I could not help but be curious, so I graphed the Ordinal Number (i.e. data point sequence number) vs. the Median Percent from this table with the following remarkable result.

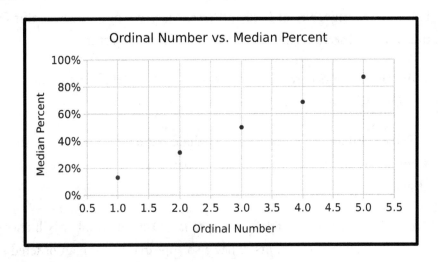

Figure E-1: Linearity of Median Percents (5 points)

I was stunned by the obvious linearity of Median Percent with data-point Ordinal Number. I wondered if this was peculiar to five data-points, and performed similar graphs based on published Median Percent for 3, 4, 5 and 6 data-points with the following result:

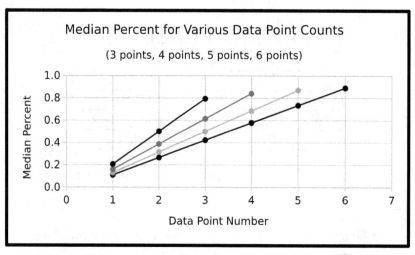

Figure E-2: Linearity of Median Percent (In General)

It became obvious that linearity of Median Percent with Ordinal Number is a statistical reality of data-sets. The Linear Conjecture of Median Percent dependence on data-point Ordinal Number was thus born. Observations Related to the Linear Conjecture:

- The N Median Percents corresponding to a set of N ordered data points are linear with respect to Ordinal Number (i.e. data-point location number 1st to last).

- Median Percent values corresponding to Ordinal Number 1 varied with the total count of data-points in the data-set. Those 1st Median Percent values seem to form an ordered sequence.

- The Median Percent values corresponding to last Ordinal Number N likewise varied with the total count of data-points. They also appeared to form an ordered sequence.

I was soon able to derive a closed form solution for the 1st and Last Median Percents using probability theory. Two equations were created:

Eq E-1 $$1stMedian\% = 1 - .5^{\left(\frac{1}{N}\right)}$$

Eq E-2 $$LastMedian\% = .5^{\left(\frac{1}{N}\right)}$$

242

It became clear that for any chosen data-set size:

- The x,y of the first point in Figure E-2 was a preordained function of point count N.

- The x,y of the last point in Figure E-2 was likewise.

Writing an equation that passes through two known points is an algebra problem requiring:

- Determine slope m from the two known data points.

- Use slope intercept equation y = mx + b. Substitute m, x1 and y1 to determine b.

- Write the general equation y=mx+b using values for m and b determined above.

When these steps are performed, the Linear Conjecture based closed form equations for computing Median Percent as a function of Ordinal Number and data-point count N results:

Eq E-3

Eq E-4

Eq E-5

$$m = \left[2 \cdot .5^{\left(\frac{1}{N}\right)} - 1\right] \cdot \left[\frac{1}{(N-1)}\right]$$

$$b = .5^{\left(\frac{1}{N}\right)} - \left[\frac{(2 \cdot N)}{(N-1)}\right] \cdot \left[.5^{\left(\frac{1}{N}\right)} - .5\right]$$

$$MedianPercent = m \cdot i + b$$

Where i = Data Point Number of interest

N = Total number of data-points

Separation of the closed form Linear Conjecture equation into 3 lines as shown above, is extremely convenient for real world problems. Substitution for m and b determines an equivalent "one line" equation as follows:

$$MedianPrct = \left[2 \cdot .5^{\left(\frac{1}{N}\right)} - 1 \right] \cdot \left[\frac{1}{(N-1)} \right] \cdot i + .5^{\left(\frac{1}{N}\right)} - \left[\frac{(2 \cdot N)}{(N-1)} \right] \cdot \left[.5^{\left(\frac{1}{N}\right)} - .5 \right]$$

Eq E-6: Expression of Linear Conjecture Equation

Applicability: The above equations produce accurate results for data-sets consisting of any number N data-points. The Ordinal Number (i.e. data-point number normally 1, 2, 3, ...N) used in equations above can take on any rational value greater than or equal to one, less than or equal to N (see notes 5 & 6). The use of fractional Ordinal Numbers (such as the 2.25th data point) is common (and allowed) when test specimens are prematurely removed from life testing. Such fractional ordinal numbers are justified by either probability theory, or as linear adjustments applied to a progressively dwindling test sample population(2)(3).

Interpolation based on tabular values of Median Percent are the traditional way of creating Median Percents for fractional ordinal numbers. The method, with little justification has long been used. If accepted, the Linear Conjecture firmly establishes a basis for linearity of decimal ordinal number locations between whole number sequenced data-points. Extension of The Linear Conjecture to decimal ordinal number locations is equivalent to traditional practice and appears justified by The Linear Conjecture.

Two traditional methods exist for creating decimal ordinal numbers associated with discarded (or suspended) data-points:

- the Leonard Jones Method

- the Bompas-Smith Method

Both methodologies use linearisation of Median Percents for non-integer Ordinal Number data-points. The Leonard Jones Method uses simple probability assumptions to adjust actual fail sequence. The Bompas-Smith method applies direct linearisation to adjust fail increment

Linearisation is implicit in both traditional rank adjustment methods and suggests acceptance of linearisation between non-integer values of ordinal number. Given implicit acceptance of linearisation by tradition, use of The Linear Conjecture for adjusted ordinals is feits accomplis.

Formal Mathematical Proof vs. Brute Force Justification:

Various approaches have been tried to provide a formal mathematical proof of The Linear Conjecture; but, tight statistical justification always seems to return to the Binomial Equation. When describing a data-set of N points, the Binomial equation contains N+1 terms of the general form:

$$\text{Eq E-7} \qquad \boxed{\sum \left[Cons\tan t \cdot p^k \cdot q^{(N-k)} \right] where Cons\tan t =_a C_b}$$

 Because data-sets contain a dozen or more points, 12th (and higher) order equations result which are only solvable by trial and error. High order binomial terms render algebraic manipulations to justify the Linear Conjecture near impossible. In response, the "brute force" justification below was created.

Brute Force Justification:

The Linear Conjecture was used to compute Median Percents for a data-set of size N. Each Median Percent was substituted into properly chosen terms of the binomial (see Appendix D for needed terms). If the proposed Median Percents are correct, the Binomial Equation summation of terms will compute .50 for every Median Percent. This process was repeated for data-sets ranging from 3 points to 1000 points using a Python computer loop. For each data-set size and data-point, computed median percents were displayed along with the computed summation. After completion of all Median Percent evaluations, the worst case difference from the .50 rule was reported.

Multiple computer runs were performed with various maximum data-set sizes as documented in Table E-2 below. It may be seen from the table, that:

- Deviations of check sum from .50 are vanishingly small (see Maximum Sum Error)

- A data-set of 1000 points did not significantly increase check sum violation

Data-Size Range	Target	MaxSumErr	RunTimeSec
3-20	.50	8.88e-16	5.9
3-50	.50	4.66e-15	35.9
3-100	.50	1.144e-14	132.4
3-250	.50	3.059e-14	3927.6
3-1000	.50	1.213e-13	56560.9

Table E-2: Linear Conjecture Error Sum

Conclusions Regarding Brute Force Justification:

- Accuracy assessment for the Linear Conjecture method is difficult because results can only be compared to tables created by trial and error solution of the binomial equation. The trial and error "exit" criteria for tables is rarely documented.

- It appears Linear Conjecture generated Median Percent values are accurate beyond 4 or more decimal places. The check sum (Maximum Sum Error) of Table E-2 does not indicate error of computed Median Percent; but rather, check sum errors of binomial terms. Evidence suggests The Linear Conjecture is perfectly accurate, surpassing all other methods.

- Computation of Median Percent by the Linear Conjecture involves few calculations. Computation of check sum errors involves far more calculation and is thus suspect as primary source of "check sum" error originating from round off error. The Python language uses double precision variables by default, and thus validation calculations are very accurate.

General Conclusions:

- The Linear Conjecture stating that data-point Median Percent has linear dependence on Ordinal Number for each associated data-point has been shown true for rational values of Ordinal Number (i.e. it works for data-points 1,2, 3, 4, ... 1000).

- Equations that precisely compute the Median Percent values based on functional dependence of Ordinal Number have been derived and presented.

- The Linear Conjecture methods presented herein provide an exact alternative to the commonly used Benard Approximations. Linear Conjecture methods are believed more accurate than any other known method or table.

- The Linear Conjecture Equations enable direct computation of Median Percent for decimal values (e.g. 3.5th) of Ordinal Number.

- A brute force validation of Linear Conjecture determinations for data-sets ranging from 3 to 1000 data-points has been performed. All validations indicate extreme accuracy of the Linear Conjecture. It is believed infinitesimal check sum errors (on the order of .00000000000004) are primarily the result of round-off error inherent within validation rather than round-off within Median Percent computation.

Addendum:

A Python computer program was created and evaluated all median percents for data-sets ranging from 3 to 1000 data-points. For each point, median percent and check sum were printed. Worst case check sum error relative to .500 was reported and is miniscule. A Python program listing used to produce these results is provided below. To use: Revise line 9 (N=1000) to maximum size data-set (i.e. N) to be evaluated.

Validation of Linear Conjecture accuracy was based on the binomial method and is in accordance with Appendix D.

Note: Python programming language was used because of its extremely accurate variables and its ability to perform combinatorial mathematics. The author had not previously used the Thonny IDE for Python; but, it performed well and was easy to use. A listing of the validation program is shown below:

```python
import scipy.special
import time
time1=time.time()

print()
maxDeviant=-22
worstSum=.50

N=1000 # maximum number of data points
for h in range(3,N+1): # compute error sum for dataset sizes 3 to N
    sum=0
    print("data-set size=",h)
    for i in range(1,h+1): # evaluate median percent for ever data point
location
        # Linear Conjecture determines Median Percent Value
        m=(2*pow(.5,1/h)-1)/(h-1)
        b=pow(.5,1/h)-((2*h)/(h-1))*(pow(.5,1/h)-.5)
        p=m*i+b
        q=1-p
        sum=0
        for j in range(1,h-i+1+1): # compute term probability and sum
            coef=scipy.special.comb(h,h-j+1)
            sum=sum+coef*pow(p,h-j+1)*pow(q,j-1)
        print("size=",h,"DataPoint=",i,"Median%=",p,"Probability
Sum=",sum)
    if abs(.50-sum)>maxDeviant:
        maxDeviant=abs(.5-sum)
        worstSum=sum

time2=time.time()
print("WorstSum=",worstSum,"MaxDeviant = ",maxDeviant)
print("run time seconds = ", time2-time1)
quit()
```

Figure E-3: Python Listing for Linear Conjecture Validation

Appendix E Footnotes:

1. Median Percent Table in Appendix E was extracted from The New Weibull Handbook, Author and Publisher Dr. Robert B. Abernethy, Copyright 1993, North Palm Beach Florida

2. Numerous sources provide probability based interpretations of Leonard Jones Method Adjusted Rank Numbers (i.e. fractional Ordinal Numbers) based on the possible failure positions for each suspended data-point.

3. J. H. Bompas-Smith provides a discussion of linearly adjusted Rank Numbers (i.e. fractional Ordinal Numbers) in his book Mechanical Survival: the use of reliability data Edited by R. H. W. Brook pages 16-20.

4. Appendix E was drafted to demonstrate general applicability of the Linear Conjecture; however, the Python Program shown in Figure E-4 can also be used to determine Median Percents for a data-set of N data-points. Adjust line 9 to the desired number of data-points. Screen printouts will list each data-point along with computed Median Percent.

5. Laboratory determined data-sets often include prematurely removed test articles in response to lab equipment breakdown. When handling such data, the Ordinal Number (referred to as Order or Rank Number in The New Weibull Handbook) is adjusted to statistically reflect the effective Ordinal Number of data-points. These adjustments usually result in fractional Ordinal Numbers (e.g. 2.25).

6. In current practice analysts routinely use Median Percents created by the Benard Approximation. With release of this paper, they would be better served by using results of the Linear Conjecture.

7. At numerous locations, this paper may seem to disparage the approximate Benard Equation. While this paper concludes the Linear Conjecture is more accurate and well justified, the author has no wish to criticize the Benard Equation or its creator. Computations by the Benard Equation generally have less than 1% error, and in the absence of anything better, have served well for many years.

Appendix F: Data Point Count & Weibull Accuracy

Warning: The following is a preliminary study and the results should not be regarded as authoritative. This study was conducted to identify future research opportunities. My reading of Weibull literature has not identified means of establishing the needed number of data points to reliably estimate β and η for a population.

The Need for Accuracy Descriptions:

There seems to be no guidance regarding the number of data-points needed to achieve a specified accuracy for Weibull Beta and Eta parameters. While confidence bounds provide a level of insight, they do not meet the needs of industry and science.

- Confidence bounds are provided "after the fact" thus offering no "up front" direction regarding the number of samples that should be put into test, or the number of real world data points needed during field data collection.

- Confidence bounds analyze apparent consistency of data, but have no means of determining whether "dumb luck" may have provided a well behaved data-set not representative of the actual population. An example would be a series of data-points that are consistently below typical values.

Confidence Bounds Example:

Confidence bounds are typically displayed as curved lines both above and below the fitted line corresponding to data-points. Confidence bounds are constructed to be 90% (or other value) likely to contain the true data-point fitted line corresponding to the actual data population. An example is provided below showing 90% Confidence Bounds. This plot was created by the Watson-Weibull program.

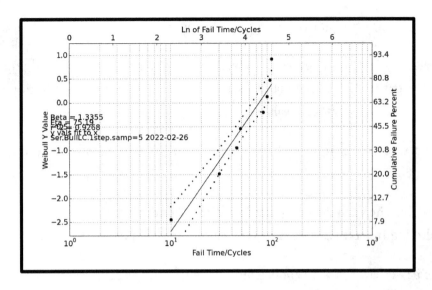

Figure F-1: 90% Confidence Bounds about Data-point

Shortfalls in the confidence bound approach led to the development of this preliminary study.

Preliminary Study Definition:

A preliminary study has been performed using small data-sets to determine the feasibility of developing the desired relationship. The study was constructed as follows:

- Evaluation data point counts 3, 5, 10, 15, 20, 25, 30, 50, 75 and 100 were established.

- For each evaluation data point count, five repeated experiments based on randomly selected data-sets of the required size were obtained. Each data-set was picked from a computer synthesized population of 500 Weibull points having Eta of 10 and Beta values 1, 2 and 3.5

- Scatter plots (x=data point count and y=determined values of Beta and Eta) were prepared for visual examination. At each evaluation data point count, five results (e.g. 5

251

inferred Betas) were plotted. See graphs below.

- Several analysis approaches were applied to scatter plots. Ultimately, all points were plotted together (once for Beta and separately for Eta) to enable definition of an envelop of (near) worst case values.

- It was determined that upper bound percent errors were roughly twice as large as lower bound percent values.

- Regression line analysis was applied to selected envelop points using both power law and also log functions. A power law equation provided a better model.

- While power law fits were applied and achieved $R^2 > 98\%$, release has not been made of final conclusions, because a study of broader scope is needed prior to reliance on determined functional relationships between data-point count and maximum percent error expected of parameters Beta and Eta.

Needed Study Improvements:

While the preliminary study is promising, the results enabled identification of needed improvements prior to release of a formal study with conclusions.

- For each of the evaluation data point counts, five repeat experiments (based on distinct data-sets) were performed to determine Beta and Eta. Scatter plots suggest that 5 repeat experiments is insufficient. Any future study should employ 50 to 100 repeat experiments to minimize "data jitter".

- Some dependency of error on Beta is apparent with Beta=1 typically exhibiting wider spreads in scatter plots. Future studies should use a greater range of Beta.

- Separate characterizations based on different Betas should be performed.

- It may be worthwhile to analyze scatter plots as Weibull distributions.

Scatter Plots:

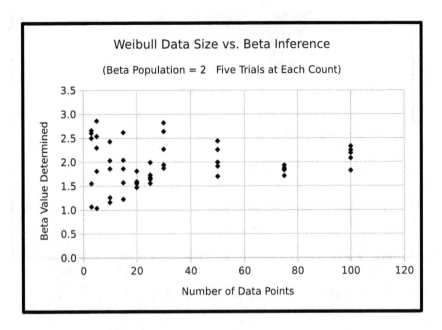

Figure F-2: Data-set Size vs. Beta Inferences

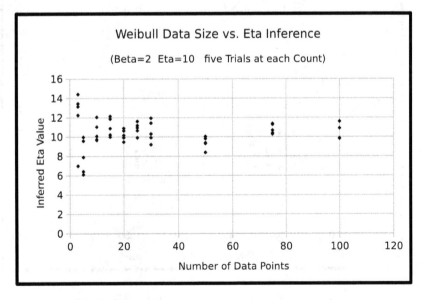

Figure F-3: Data-set Size vs. Eta Inference

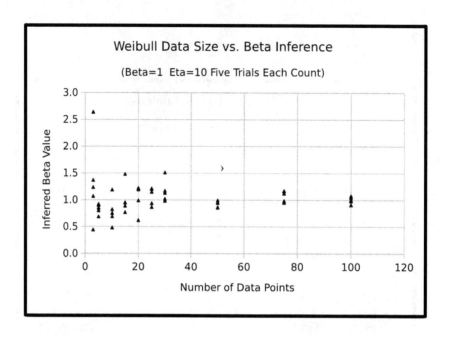

Figure F-4: Data-set Size vs. Beta Inferences

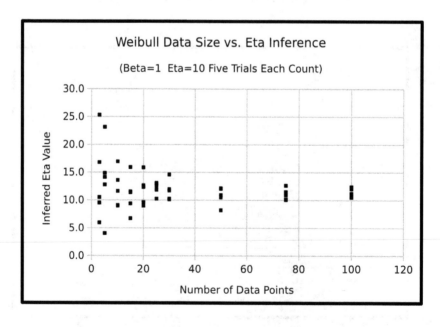

Figure F-5: Data-set Size vs. Eta Inferences

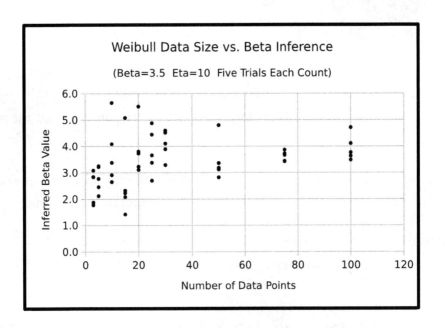

Figure F-6: Data-set Size vs. Beta Inference

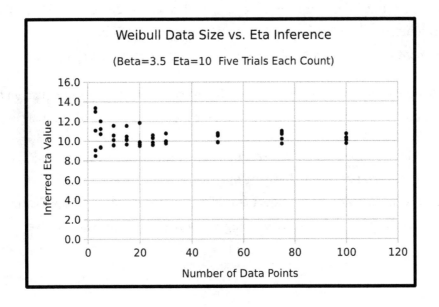

Figure F-7: Data-set Size vs. Eta Inference

Conclusions:

- In all cases, smaller data-set sizes show wider percent error variation and larger data-set sizes show smaller variation (of inferred Beta and/or Eta). This means that all graphs above appear like a funnel with the big end at the 3 data-point end and the small end at 100 data-point end.

- Erratic "up and down jitter" between the adjacent data-sets indicates a need for much larger numbers of repeat experimental Beta/Eta inference (5 is not enough).

- In general, Beta percent errors above the "known population value" exceed errors below. At 5 data-points, upper errors are about double and at the 100 point end are close to equal in value.

- Generally, small Beta values exhibit greater inferred Beta and Eta percent errors.

- All data-point inferred Betas were graphed together to enable enveloping of extreme points. For Beta and Eta (both upper and lower) a power law function of repeat experiment count was fit to the envelop. In all cases, R^2 exceeded 95%. This activity was conducted using "eyeball" selection of points, but it is believed increasing repeat experiment count from 5 to 50 would enable a more systematic approach.

- It is believed this study shows it is possible to create a closed form equation specifying the number of data-points needed to achieve a desired degree of accuracy.

- Public release of functional relationships between data-point count and percent error in Beta and Eta are not released as part of this study, because its preliminary nature and small data-set size do not provide a confident basis for real world application. Some insight can be gathered from examining the scatter plots provided above.

This Page Intentionally left blank

Appendix G: Weibull Studies
(A list of conducted Weibull studies)

Various studies were conducted in support of this book. The following is a partial listing of such studies, their purpose and the method used.

1. Linear Conjecture: Develops alternative closed form solution for Median Percent values corresponding to 1st, 2nd, 3rd ... nth data points of a collection of n data points. The development is based on review of data sets for 3 through 1000 data points. The generalized closed form solution was demonstrated correct for positive rational values of data point Ordinal Number. Appendix E presents brute force validation consisting of a Python test of all Median Percents for data-set sizes from 3 to 1000 data-points.

2. Relationship between Data-Point Count and Accuracy of Weibull Analysis Characterization of Population #1: The analysis strives to determine how many data points are required to achieve an acceptable and dependable level of accuracy in estimating the underlying data set Weibull parameters. The method used was to repeatedly evaluate computer generated Weibull synthetic data sets of known parameters β and η. Numerous trials were run in a computer loop to determine the effect on accuracy of result in terms of β, η and R^2. This analysis utilized python based code titled "ManyDataWeibPlotB.py". This particular study was for concept validation only, and results are tentative, as a larger collection of data-runs is needed. Proof of concept appears promising. Program was written using Python version 2.7

3. Variation of data-point range resulting from random value selection from established Weibull population of known β and η was evaluated. The purpose was to determine the likely range of randomly selected 1st, 2nd ... nth data points. Studies were made using a computer generated synthetic data set of known Weibull characteristics. Both the data set and the resulting range determination was accomplished by a python program "ManyDataSets200G.py". Program written using Python 2.7

4. Probability of occurrence for randomly selected data points was evaluated. It was assumed that data-point selection is a Gaussian distributed variable about the population mean value. The concurrent probability of data points was evaluated. No conclusive results were determined. The method used program dataDriftA.py, a pythonista program implemented on iPad.

5. An additional Python program was developed/modified that enabled empirical determination of Median Percents. The program was ManyDataWeibPlotD.py. Program written using Python 2.7

6. The program Z119.py is the most advanced version of the Watson-Weibull program and was used to produce Watson-Weibull information, Weibull Plots, menus etc. Program written using Python 2.7

7. The program LCValidatorRevE.py was written in Python Rev 3.7. The program uses the Linear Conjecture to compute Median Percent, and then verifies its correctness via the binomial equation (which is explained in Appendix D). The program implements loops to evaluate every Median Percent for data-sets of size 3 points up to 1000 points depending on the N variable which is established on line 9 of the listing.

8. A tentative study was begun to determine the extent of "z data trending" that is permissible to ensure not more than 15% change in determined Weibull Beta value. The study is ongoing and may not be completed for inclusion in this document. It seems likely that mathematical analysis in lieu of computer analysis may suffice.

Appendix H: Useful Equations & Derivations

Appendix H provides a summary of the most often used Weibull equations.

Computation of 1st and Last Median Percents for N total data points:

$$1stMedian\% = 1 - .5^{\left(\frac{1}{N}\right)}$$
$$LastMedian\% = .5^{\left(\frac{1}{N}\right)}$$

Weibull 2 Parameter PDF Equation: (note: often expressed using neg exponent)

$$2ParameterPDF: f(t) = \beta \cdot \frac{t^{(\beta - 1)}}{\eta^{\beta}} \cdot e^{\left(-\left(\frac{t}{\eta}\right)^{\beta}\right)}$$

Weibull 2 Parameter CDF Equation: (note: expressed using neg exponent)

$$F(x) = 1 - e^{-\left(\frac{x}{\eta}\right)^{\beta}}$$

Weibull 3 Parameter PDF Equation: (note: often expressed using neg exponent)

$$PDF - 3parameter: f(x) = \left(\beta \cdot \frac{(X - Xo)^{(\beta - 1)}}{(\eta^{\beta})}\right) \cdot \frac{1}{e^{\left(\left(\frac{(X - Xo)}{\eta}\right)^{\beta}\right)}}$$

$$1stMedian\% = 1 - .5^{\left(\frac{1}{N}\right)}$$

$$CDF - 3parameter: F(x) = 1 - \frac{1}{e^{\left(\left(\frac{(X - Xo)}{\eta}\right)^{\beta}\right)}}$$

Determining Median Value from Median Percent, Beta and Eta:

$$F(x) = 1 - \frac{1}{e^{\left(\frac{x}{\eta}\right)^{\beta}}} \rightarrow x = \eta \cdot \left[-\ln(1 - F(x))\right]^{\left(\frac{1}{\beta}\right)}$$

Linear Conjecture Equations: to determine Median Percents

$$m = \left[2 \cdot .5^{\left(\frac{1}{N}\right)} - 1\right] \cdot \left[\frac{1}{(N-1)}\right]$$

$$b = .5^{\left(\frac{1}{N}\right)} - \left[\frac{(2 \cdot N)}{(N-1)}\right] \cdot \left[.5^{\left(\frac{1}{N}\right)} - .5\right]$$

$$MedianPercent = m \cdot i + b$$

Linear Conjecture Equation (Consolidated as 1 Equation)

$$MedPrct = \left[2 \cdot .5^{\left(\frac{1}{N}\right)} - 1\right] \cdot \left[\frac{1}{(N-1)}\right] \cdot i + .5^{\left(\frac{1}{N}\right)} - \left[\frac{(2 \cdot N)}{(N-1)}\right] \cdot \left[.5^{\left(\frac{1}{N}\right)} - .5\right]$$

Benard's Approximation Equation: to estimate Median Percents

$$Median\% \sim \frac{(i - .3)}{(N + .4)}$$

Binomial Equation Example (for four event occurrences)

$$1p^4 \cdot q^0 + 4p^3 \cdot q^1 + 6p^2 \cdot q^2 \cdot 4p^1 \cdot q^3 + 1p^0 \cdot q^4 = 100\%$$

Where is the MTBF in Weibull? (only if Beta=1 is it true)

$$MTBF = 1/\lambda$$
$$MTBF = \eta weib$$

Appendix J: Small Sample Analysis Examples:

Appendix J is a cautionary notice to analysts not to "oversell" what Weibull analysis can do. "Over selling" often occurs when an analyst is squeezed between management demands for less testing and the analyst's need for more data.

As a first example, experiments to determine the distribution of apple weight were repeated four times, and the consistency of results compared. The experiments were repeated using cumquats and a summary characterizing consistency of results is presented.

To draw attention to the issue of small data-sets, a simple experiment was performed in my kitchen resulting in a small data-set. An experiment to determine the distribution was performed four times and one would hope that all four "runs" would draw similar and accurate conclusions about the underlying population. The results did not turn out that way. Unpredictability of all statistical methods (including Weibull) is the result of "random data drift" which often occurs when small data-sets are analyzed.

A second example is presented in which earthquake population characterization based on a 2005 study is compared to results of a much larger data-set from a 2012 study. Both data-sets were for the Cascadia Subduction Zone off the Oregon/Washington coast and many of the participating geologists were the same. These two studies provide an example of how better and larger data-sets may alter population characterization.

The Pitfall of Bad Predictions:

A wise man once said, "Nothing is more destructive to a young engineer's career than making a bad prediction; because, after the first, no one will believe him." It is thus important to learn the limitations of Weibull analysis to avoid "overselling" the results. Several chapters address the rather tenuous trends assessed by Weibull but Appendix J provides stark examples.

The Danger of Small Data Sets:

While Weibull analysis methods are legitimate, analysis of data-sets (by any statistical method) may incorrectly characterize the underlying population of objects/events. The problem is acute for small data sets (less than 20 data points) and sometimes results in inaccurate predictions. When a Normal (Gaussian) population is analyzed, the population is described by its Mean Value (i.e. the average) and its Standard Deviation. For 2 parameter Weibull distributions, the population is described by shape parameter β (beta), and by scale parameter η (eta). Mischaracterization of the parent population thus refers to computation of β and η values which do not accurately describe the parent population. Appendix J provides real world examples showing small data sets are error prone. It demonstrates the tendency for inferred β and η to drift away from reality when 5 samples are used.

Note: There is no magical "cut-off" number of required data-points. Five data-points are very likely to produce poor results. Ten data-points are better, but still risky. At around 20 data-points, preliminary studies indicate most of the results will be acceptable, and outliers are less than horrid.

Concepts of Shape Parameter Beta and Scale Parameter Eta:

Drift of β and η away from true values demands an intuitive concept of β and η.

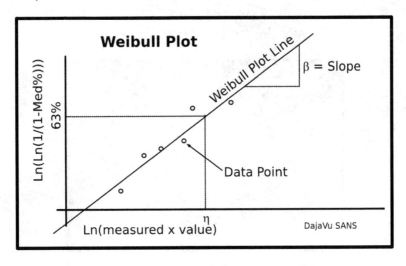

Figure J-1: Concept of Slope Beta and Eta

Ignoring the details of creation (see Chapter 4), β is the slope of a "best fit" straight line through the data points as shown above. η is the raw x value corresponding to 63% cumulative. For example, if a Weibull Distribution describes the life span of people, η is the age by which 63% of the population will have died. Obviously, the average life span will be somewhat less than η years. For a 2 parameter Weibull, parameters β and η fully describe the distribution much like Mean and Standard Deviation do for a Normal Distribution.

Analysis of Apple Samples:

Below, I analyze weight for a population of 16 grocery store "rocket red apples"as follows:

- Determine Beta and Eta by creating a Weibull Plot for all 16 Apples

- Experiment 1: Determine Beta and Eta based on a random sample of 5 apples.

- Experiment 2: After replacing and mixing apples, the experiment is repeated with 5 apples. Determine ...

- Experiment 3: Ditto

- Experiment 4: Ditto

If a sample of 5 fruits reliably produces good results, we should expect steps b through e to produce β and η values consistently close to actual values from step a. The results follow:

Figure J-2: Experimental Set-up

Step 1: Determine 16 Apple Population β and η values by Weibull Plot.

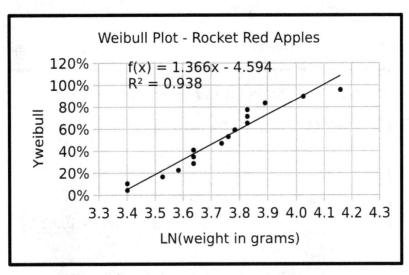

Figure J-3: Apple Population Weibull Plot β=1.369 η=28.88

Baseline Experiment All 16 Samples: β is read directly from the fitted equation's slope. η is computed as 2.71828^(-intercept/Beta). "Ratty" data-points approximate a straight line, with R^2 =93.8%. Since R^2 >90%, Weibull approximates the weight distribution. We proceed with repeat experiments using 5 data-points to determine dependability Weibull inference.

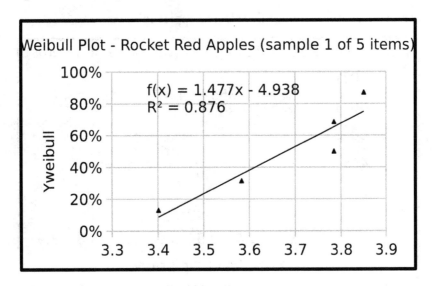

Figure J-4: Apple Test #1 Weibull Plot β=1.477 η=28.8

Weibull Plot J-4 with low R^2 value is of concern. Based on known population values, we know β and η estimates are good, but inference of β and η when R^2 < 90% is unacceptable.

Second Experiment: Once again based on a sample of five randomly selected apples:

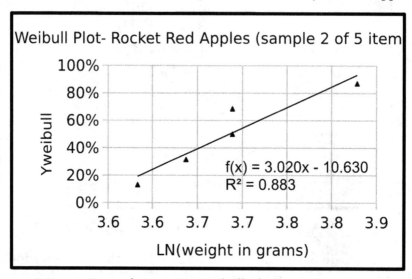

Figure J-5: Apple Test #2 Weibull Plot β=3.02 η=33.8

Figure J-5 R^2 <90% again signals that estimates of β and η are "trash".

Third Experiment: Test #3 of five randomly selected apples follows:

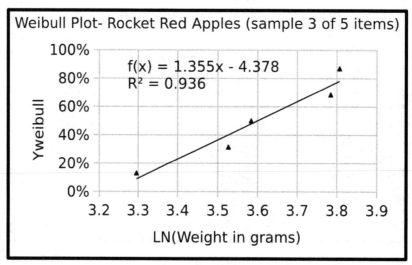

Figure J-6: Apple Test #3 Weibull Plot: β=1.35 η=25.3

Third Experiment Figure J-5 has an R^2 value of 93.6% and fitted data points are consistent with the fitted line. Based on this evidence, the Weibull Plot inferred β and η values should be correct as confirmed by our "special knowledge" of the actual population.

Fourth Experiment: Sample of five randomly selected apples follows:

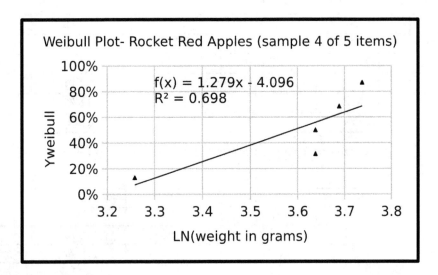

Figure J-7: Apple Test #4 Weibull Plot: β=1.279 η=24.59

Fourth Experiment Figure J-6 has an R^2 = 69.8%. Usually, low values indicate poor estimates of β and η. Scatter of the data points leaves us wondering whether the lowest data point is legitimate. Despite worrying observations, inferred β has only 6% error and η 15% error. These are unexpectedly good results given the poor R^2 value

Cumquat Experiments:

A very similar fruit experiment was performed with 15 cumquats. The results of four experiments using five randomly picked samples is shown in Table J-2 below.

Conclusions from Eight Fruit Experiments:

Four experiments involving five apple samples extracted from a population of known β and n were performed to determine the dependability of small data set inference. Four additional experiments were performed in a similar manner with cumquats. The results of all eight experiments are summarized in Tables J-1 and J-2 below.

	Beta	Beta Err	Eta	Eta Err	R^2
Apple Pop.	1.3659	0%	28.88	0%	94%
Exp #1	1.4774	8%	28.28	2%	88%
Exp #2	3.0200	>100%	33.78	17%	88%
Exp #3	1.3552	1%	25.29	12%	94%
Exp #4	1.2794	6%	24.56	15%	70%

Table J-1: Results of 4 Apple Population Characterization Experiments

	Beta	Beta Err	Eta	Eta Err	R^2
Comq. Pop.	1.1615	0%	4.32	0%	
Exp #1	0.6881	32%	3.65	16%	90%
Exp #2	2.1923	89%	4.75	10%	80%
Exp #3	1.0299	11%	4.18	3%	93%
Exp #4	1.366	18%	5.36	24%	90%

Table J-2: Results of 4 Cumquat Population characterization Experiments

Fruit Experiment Conclusions:

Of 8 experiments, only four produced $R^2 >= 90\%$ which typically indicates credible results. Based on the author's experience, we should expect somewhat more "credible results".

Of the 4 experiments with $R^2 >= 90\%$, only two had acceptable accuracy for both β and n. Both of the acceptable experiments exhibited $R^2 >= 93\%$. Inconsistency of results from these 8 experiments are an indictment of small data sets rather than the Weibull method. Weibull accuracy improves with larger data sets and when $R^2 >= 93\%$. Experiments with $R^2 < 90\%$ produce unpredictable results.

Based on hundreds of analyses performed during a preliminary study (see Appendix F), a minimum 20 of data points is recommended to produce reasonable results for β and η; but, there is no sharp dividing line between good and bad. 30 data points is better than 20. R^2 <90% often results in dreadfully wrong β and η inference. When R^2 >93% results become more reliable. Statistical methods (confidence bounds) do exist which are intended to identify the range of credible β and η population values and are discussed in various chapters. Fruit Experiment Conclusions differ from some authors who claim Weibull methods are effective when applied to small data-sets. While the methods are workable, extreme caution is advised when data sets are small.

An Important World Event:

The reader may wonder whether there are more important uses for Weibull than fruit experiments. From the Oregon State University Newsroom: Corvallis, Or. July 30, 2012, "A comprehensive analysis of the Cascadia Subduction Zone off the Pacific northwest coast confirms that the region has had numerous earthquakes over the past 10,000 years, and suggests that the southern Oregon coast may be the most vulnerable... Written by researchers at Oregon State University ... the study concludes that there is a 40% chance of a major earthquake ... in the next 50 years. And that earthquake could approach the intensity of the Tohoku quake that devastated Japan in March of 2011." (1) When such a quake occurs, it will affect tens of thousands of people and result in billions of dollars of damage. This is perhaps the reason why 13 years of research, extensive off coast core samples and legions of geologists were engaged to get improved data that resulted in these conclusions. Comparison of these predictions with analysis based on previously available and smaller data-sample demonstrates how data quality and quantity can alter analysis results:

From 2003 and 2005 Research Studies: Wikipedia presents the following estimates of year intervals between major earthquakes during the last 3500 years. (2)

From 2005 Research Studies: Wikipedia presents the following estimates of year intervals between major earthquakes during the last 3500 years. (2)

2005 Source(3)	2003 Source(4)	Interval Years
1700 AD	1700 AD	780
780-1190 AD	880-960 AD	210
690-730 AD	550-750 AD	330
350-420 AD	250-320 AD	910
660-440 BC	610-450 BC	400
960-890 BC	910-780BC	250
1140-1340 BC	1150-1220 BC	Unknown

Table J-4: 2005 Report Earthquake Intervals

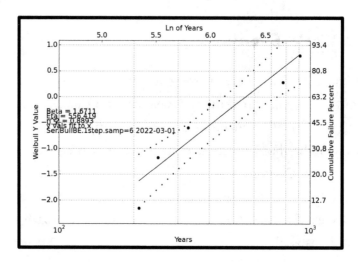

Figure J-8: Watson-Weibull generated plot

The Weibull Plot above resulted from 6 data points of the 2005 geologic study. In the figure below, a Weibull Plot based on a more extensive data-set of 39 points over a 10 thousand year period and supported by extensive off shore core sampling provides improved data-point accuracy and represents a wider range of time with the following result.

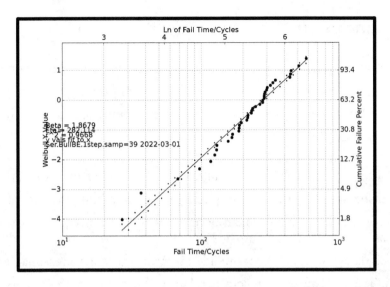

Figure J-9: Watson Weibull generated plot

The significant differences of the two Weibull plots above are:

The 2nd plot represents 39 earthquakes over 10 thousand years (i.e., much more data). It has large regions where data points fall almost on top of the line. The 96% R^2 value is far better than in Figure J-8. Beta has increased from 1.6711 to 1.8679 and perhaps the largest difference is the change in Eta from 556.4 years to 287.1 years. The updated Eta value indicates that 63% of repeat earthquakes should occur within 287 years of the prior event.

A Future Prediction:

Using the methods presented in Chapters 8 and 10, the probability of a major earthquake off the Oregon coast during the next 50 years can be determined. An analysis was performed by the author using records during the last 10 thousand years. My analysis indicates 40% likelihood which matches predictions of geologists at Oregon State University.

Figures J-8 and J-9 were created using a 2 Parameter Weibull Analysis. Some improvement may be possible if a 3 parameter Weibull Analysis is applied. Using the larger data-set, the 3 parameter analysis produces a similar Eta value, with a bit higher Beta value and somewhat improved R^2. The results are not substantially different.

Appendix j Conclusions:

1. Small data-sets are likely to produce inaccurate assessments of underlying population characteristics. For five sample data-sets, repeat experiments for only four out of eight experiments resulted in Beta values approximating actual population values. This suggests only a 50% likelihood of characterizing Beta with five data-points.

2. Weibull is not uniquely susceptible to small data-set induced errors. All statistical methods are equally affected because the problem originates from likely "misbehavior" of data-points. As data-point count increases, this problem becomes less pronounced.

3. Not less than 20 data-points are recommended in order to achieve reasonable results using Weibull Analysis. The 20 data-point recommendation is based on a preliminary study presented in Appendix F.

4. Confidence bounds do not completely address the risk of data-point drift for small data-sets; however, such bounds are the best available method of estimating likely range of Beta and Eta values for the analyzed population.

5. When R^2 values are less than 90%, the use of Weibull Plot results is not recommended as estimates of Beta and Eta are likely to be poor. Results become considerably better when $R^2 > 93\%$. R^2 values exceeding 98% usually produce data-points with little scatter over much of the x variable range.

6. Weibull methods do enable useful characterization of populations and provide a basis for future predictions provided care is exercised in the quality and quantity of data.

Footnotes:

1. "13- year Cascadia study complete – and earthquake risk looms large", Oregon State University Newsroom, Source Chris Goldfinger, July 30, 2012

2. "Cascadia subduction zone", Wikipedia. See Earthquake timing table of estimated year and interval

3. "The Orphan Tsunami of 1700 – Japanese Clues to a Parent Earthquake in North America", by Atwater et. al., U.S. Geological Survey Professional Paper 1707 ed., University of Washington Press 2005

4. "Earthquake "Recurrence Inferred from Paleoseismology", by Atwater et. al. Published by Developments in Quaternary Science 2003

5. Weibull Plots Figures J-8 and J-9 were created using the Watson-Weibull analysis program currently under development by the author.

6. "The Use of Weibull in Defect Data Analysis", by Warwick Manufacturing Group, December 2004

7. "Statistical Reliability Analysis Manual for the Weibull-DR", by applications Research, Inc. Minnesota

8. For a discussion of earthquake age estimation methods, see "Recurrence Intervals for Great Earthquakes of the Past 3500 years at Noreastern Willapa Bay Washington", by Brian Atwater and Eileen Hemhill-Haley, U.S. Geological Survey Professional Paper 1576, 1997.

Appendix K: Rank Order Adjustment Theory

When first encountered, Rank Order Adjustment methods seem to work, but the rationale behind the equations seems mysterious. Appendix K is provided to acquaint the reader with the kind of thinking behind some of these methods. There are a few ideas that are common:

The Adjusted Fail Number should in some way acknowledge the number of samples remaining in test at time of failure. This is to say that arbitrary changes in test sample count (discards) require adjustment to fail number.

Contra order is backwards numbering of test samples beginning from the last. It is a direct representation of samples remaining in test.

The expected number of items remaining in test is N-Ordinal Number

Test reported rows represent either Failures (F) or Discards/Suspensions (S). Suspensions necessitate fail increment adjustment of subsequent failures.

Bompas-Smith Increment

During test planning, the first failure is failure number 1, and each subsequent failure number is normally increased by an increment of 1. Certain circumstances require a failure increment other than 1 as discussed below.

Consider the following: If the test sample size extracted from a population were doubled, we should expect the number of failures occurring at various test times to double. The Bompas-Smith Failure Increment recognizes this need for adjustment and is conceptually based on the ratio of (Original Test Sample Size)/(Reduced Test Sample Size). Because this may seem counter intuitive, discussion follows.

One failure from a test sample size of 5 items would very likely have been 2 failures if the test sample had been twice as large. In fact, we should expect that as test sample size increases, test failures at the same x value exposure should increase in like proportion.

Rather than increasing, test sample size usually reduces as samples are prematurely removed from test (suspensions). Given that the first failure counts as 1 (based on the original test sample size), after a suspension, the test sample size is reduced and subsequent actual failures should be scaled up and thus counted as more than one relative to the original data-set.

Each single failure from that smaller test sample counts as slightly more than one failure based on the larger original data-set. Thus, a suspension results in small, fractional increments added to failure count. The adjusted failure sequence numbers might become 1, 2.25, 3.5 ... in lieu of the original 1, 2, 3 ....

Consider a test of 5 samples subjected to test, with discards sequenced as below.

	Col A	Col B	Col C	Col D	Col E
	Ordinal No	Contra No	F/S	Fail No	
Row 1	1	5	F	1	
Row 2	2	4	S		
Row 3	3	3	F	2	
Row 4	4	2	S		
Row 5	5	1	F	3	

Table K-1: Example of Bompas-Smith Rank Adjustment

Consider the following adjustment of Row 3 Fail Number, preceded by Row 2 Discard.

Row 1: The first failure has fail increment of 1 based on a data size of 5 items.

Row 3: Having failed an item in Row 1, the 2nd actual failure should occur for a remaining test population of 4; but due to the discard, it occurs within a remaining population of 3.

It is thus necessary to use a fail increment of 4/3 = 1.333

2nd actual failure, is thus adjusted to become the 1+1.333 = 2.333rd failure.

Row 5: 3rd failure is similarly adjusted to determine the increment. Then the increment is added to the previous value of 2.3333

Ideas above are the basis for the Bompas-Smith fail increment adjustment method as documented in Chapter 5. In his excellent book, Bompas-Smith presents a very algebraic justification but arrives at the same conclusion shown above.

Bompas-Smith method applied to above example, Row 3:

Increment = Recent Failures * (N-PreviousFailNumber)/Contra Number

Where Recent Failure = 1

Previous Fail Number = 1

N= 5 data-points total

Contra Number=3

Then Fail Number=1* (5-1)/3=1.333

Fail Number = PriorFailNumber + 1.333 = 2.333

	Col A	Col B	Col C	Col D	Col E
	Ordinal No	Contra No	F/S	Fail No	Bompas-S.
Row 1	1	5	F	1	1
Row 2	2	4	S		
Row 3	3	3	F	2	2.333
Row 4	4	2	S		
Row 5	5	1	F	3	3.667

Table K-2: Bompas-Smith Rank Adjustment

The basis for Bompas-Smith Fail Increment has been presented, and the Bompas-Smith equation from Chapter 5 used to compute Adjusted Failure Ranks for each of three actual failure points in the table above.

A Theoretical Failure Method is developed below:

The reasoning below is similar to articles I have read about other Adjusted Failure Increment methods. It is only for explanatory purposes because it has not been:

- Offered as a serious alternative to other methods

- Reduced to close form equation

- Carefully compared to other methods.

The following data-set is provided as a basis for discussion.

Ordinal No	F/S	Fail No	Time
1	F	1	10
2	S		13
3	F	2	22
4	S		42
5	F	3	68

Table K-3: Data-Set for Conceptual Rank Adjustment Method

Assumptions:

Had it remained in test, Ordinal #2 would have failed at one of the following times

- Prior to Failure at Ordinal 3 (between 13 and 22 seconds)

- Prior to Failure at Ordinal 5 (between 22 and 68 seconds)

- After all Failures (after 68 seconds)

Had it remained in test, Ordinal #4, would have failed at one of the following times

- Prior to Failure at Ordinal 5 (between 42 and 68 seconds)

- After all Failures (after 68 seconds)

It is (boldly) assumed that all possible failure locations of a suspension are equally likely. Thus the probability of failure prior to Ordinals 2 and 4 can be calculated as the sum of probabilities of all possible prior failures. The probability sums thus determined can be used as "bump-ups" to fail increments.

There are 5 possible failure locations (all equally probable by assumption)

- There is 1 possible before actual Fail Number 2, thus a probability of 1/5 or .20

- There are 2 possible prior failures for actual Fail Number 3 thus a probability of 2/5

The fail increments used in lieu of 1 for the 2nd and 3rd actual failures are:

- Prior to Fail Number 2: only 1 way. 1/5 = .20 => increment = 1.2

- Prior to Fail Number 3: 2 possible ways. 2/5 = .40 => increment = 1.4

If these increments are used to compute Adjusted Fail Number, the following Adjusted Fail Numbers result when added to the previous Adjusted Fail Number (also called Adjusted Rank) Note: Column 4 results (this method) are compared to previous Bompas-Smith values in column 6).

Ordinal No	F/S	Fail No	Adj Fail No	Time	Bompas-S
1	F	1	1	10	1
2	S			13	
3	F	2	1+1.1=2.2	22	2.33
4	S			42	
5	F	3	2.2+1.4=3.6	68	3.67

Table K-4: Comparison of Probability Method to Bompas-Smith Method

The method offered above has not been carefully researched, and was only offered as an example of the kind of thinking used to develop fail rank-adjustment methods. Based on this one example, it is interesting that the results are not greatly different from those of the Bompas-Smith method.

Appendix L: The Use of 3 Parameter Weibulls

It was previously recommended that a 3 parameter Weibull be "tried" as an alternative to the 2 parameter Weibull (when commercial software is available). In general, the 3 parameter Weibull is preferred when:

- It eliminates arced curvature of data-points

- It significantly improves the R^2 coefficient (i.e closer to 100%)

Fulfillment of these two criteria usually (not always) justifies use of the 3 parameter Weibull. Common sense evaluation must be applied as illustrated by the following Weibull Analysis of US Male Mortality. A few issues worth consideration follow:

1. Does the original PDF distribution obviously begin at x=zero? If we are studying percentage of population dying at various ages, it is clear that no deaths occur before zero.

2. Does use of the 3 parameter distribution result in absurdly large Beta values? If data-points seem well described, but Beta=452, something is likely wrong. Beta seldom exceeds 8.

3. After determination of Beta, Eta and Xo, a CDF graph can be constructed. Does the graph indicate important remaining items at x values significantly beyond actual data-points? This question is context dependent. Prediction of significant numbers of people living beyond 100 can have catastrophic consequences. While the Weibull prediction may contain only small errors, those may be economically catastrophic to an insurance company.

How Can Data Anomalies Happen?

The reader may recall a quotation from the Weibull-DR user's manual: "Real populations are rarely exactly Weibull, Gaussian or any other known distribution. The issue is whether available distributions act as useful predictors of characteristic behavior." The reality of Weibull characterization is that we are using precise mathematics to describe a population which is often not exactly Weibull. Mirage anomalies in the Weibull Plot are possible. Common sense must ensure we are not fooled by appearances and to prevent making pronouncements that will lead to safety or economic catastrophe.

An Example of Mirage Anomalies:

The percentage of people living to various ages is important, and is well characterized by the NCHS, National Vital Statistics System. Data for 2016 was used to create both a reliability graph, and also a Weibull Analysis thereof. Because NCHS data was processed into CDF format, deconstruction and linear interpolation were applied to determine Weibull data-points needed for a 9 point Weibull Plot.

	Median Percent	X (death age)	Ln(x)	Yweibull
1	7.45%	49.04	3.8926	-2.5589
2	18.09%	63.17	4.1458	-1.6120
3	28.72%	70.85	4.2606	-1.0829
4	39.36%	76.14	4.3326	-0.6927
5	50.00%	80.34	4.3863	-0.3665
6	60.64%	83.77	4.4281	-0.0700
7	71.28%	87.05	4.4665	0.2211
8	81.91%	90.30	4.5031	0.5365
9	92.55%	94.55	4.5491	0.9545

Table L-1: US Government Male Age/Death Data

A Weibull Plot results from creating an x-y graph based on the right two columns, allowing determination of Weibull Coefficients Beta and Eta as follows:

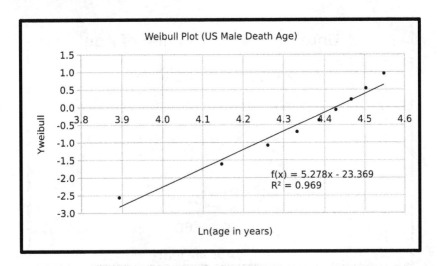

Figure L-1: Weibull Plot of Male Death Age β=5.28 η=83.85

If we ignore evident "data arcing", a CDF plot can be created based on above determined Beta and Eta hence:

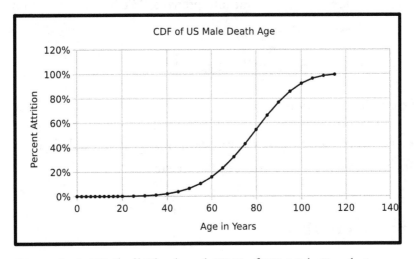

Figure L-2: Weibull Plot based CDF of US Male Death Age

The CDF above is based on Weibull Analysis. A CDF untainted by statistical distortion can be built direct from the government statistics and is shown in Figure L-3 below.

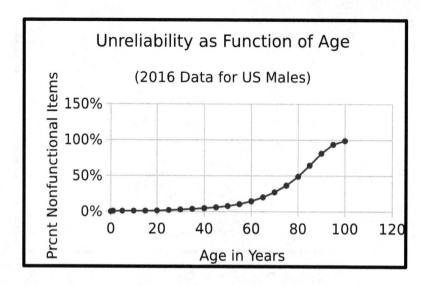

Figure L-3: CDF built directly from Government Data

Figure L2 is a CDF based on Weibull Modeling of US Government Data. Figure L3 is a CDF built directly on US Government Data (not interpreted as Weibull). Both graphs begin to "take off" at about 40 years of age; however:

- Government Data approaches 100% at age 100.

- The Weibull interpretation approaches 100% at age 110. (statistical distortion)

For many (not all) uses of statistical model Figure L-3 is "good enough," but as stated earlier such minor difference could be costly to an insurance company.

Searching for Alternatives:

Weibull Plot Figure L1 data points clearly arc about the fitted Weibull line. This often indicates need for a 3 parameter Webiull Analysis. When a 3 parameter is performed and compared to a 2 parameter Weibull Analysis the results are rather shocking.

Beta = 450   Eta=-5806   R^2=99.3%

	Spreadsheet	Spreadsheet	WeibullDR	Weibull-DR	Wat-Weib
	2 Parameter	3 Parameter	2 Parameter	3 Parameter	2 Parameter
Beta	5.2778	450.1	5.4492	453.1	5.2778
Eta	83.75	5890	83.48	5890	83.742
Xo	N/A	-5806	N/A	-5806	N/A
R^2	96.9%	99.3%	98.41 Corr	99.67 Corr	96.85%

Table L2: Comparison of 2 vs. 3 Parameter Weibull Analysis Results

Discussion:

"Arced Data" evident in Figure L1 often indicates a need for 3 parameter Weibull Analysis. Performance of the 3 parameter analysis did improve the R^2 value; however at great cost.

- Beta coefficients rarely exceed 8. Beta of 450 is utterly unexpected for the macroscopic real world (it might occur in physics particle or other extreme experiments).

- Xo=-5806 years indicates that some small percentage of the population will die almost 6000 years before they are born. This conflicts with reality.

Evidently, the underlying population is "not precisely Weibull," and this is the cause of data "arcing". Chapter 7 discussed various Weibull Plot abnormalities and their causes. Examples of "data arcing" were also shown that resulted from commingled data. The underlying data in this case is combined death ages from accidents, pneumonia, cardiac and many other causes.

We will never clearly establish the reason "data arcing" is present in Figure L1; but we may conclude:

- A 2 parameter Weibull does a moderately good job of representing the population.

- A 2 parameter Weibull is not sufficiently accurate for high age death estimates

- A 3 parameter Weibull results in a poor/awkward description of the population.

Appendix L Conclusions:

- "Arced" data points on a Weibull Plot can result from multiple causes, only one of which is the need for 3 parameter analysis.

- Common sense review of statistical (Weibull) results should always be performed to avoid "nonsense" conclusions. This is always an aspect of analysis whether statistical or otherwise. Chapter 1 presented an example of Gaussian analysis gone awry. Likewise, engineering analysts routinely check answers against intuition.

- Implausibly large Beta values and physically ridiculous Xo values usually indicate fundamental problems in Weibull Analysis or data set. This is true for both 2 parameter and 3 parameter Weibull analyses.

- "Nonsense" conclusions often result from analysis assumptions that force Weibull mathematics to start the PDF at the wrong x value, move Eta to trap actual values and contort Beta to maintain PDF area under the curve at 100%. When Weibull Analysis goes wildly wrong, it is often because we have implicitly required the equations to match an unacceptable set of conditions.

Note: Hundreds of Weibull Analyses were performed during development of this book. While most of these produced results I expected, two examples did not.

- The analysis of COVID death age statistics is an odd distribution that is not fit well by Weibull. This surprised me.

- The US Government Death Age statistics discussed above gave every indication of a 3 parameter Weibull; but, the results were horrid.

It is usually true that a 3 parameter Weibull does no harm and is often helpful. When I discovered this contrary example, I thought it worth presenting.

Appendix M: Sources of Statistical Data

1. Historical Flu Infection Rate: Centers for Disease Control (CDC): https://www.cdc.gov/flu/about/burden/past-seasons.html

2. Shark Survey: Australian Queensland Shark Research Program, https://www.daf.qld.gov.au/business-priorities/fisheries/shark-control-program

3. Naval Guns: British Battleships 1889-1904, R. A. Burt, Naval Institute Press, 1988

4. Earthquake, wind and rainfall: Japan Meteorological Society, jma.go.jp

5. Cannon, Bore Erosion: Journal of the United States Artillery, Fort Monroe, VA for period of 1892-1903

6. Rivet Strength: National Advisory Committee for Aeronautics, Wartime Report- Tests on Hydraulically Expanded Rivets, Langley Field Virginia ,1944

7. Agricultural Data: UN Food and Agricultural Organization of the United Nations: http://www.fao.org/faostat/en/#data/QC

8. Texas Cotton Yield: USDA, https://www.nass.usda.gov/Statistics_by_State/Texas/Publications/Charts_&_Maps/zcott_yp.php

9. San Juan Annual Rainfall: NOAA – National Data Buoy Center, https://www.ndbc.noaa.gov

10. Coastal Guns: Seacoast Fortifications of the United States, Emanuel Raymond Lewis, Naval Institute Press, 1970

11. Concrete Strength: Comparison of the Compressive Strength of Concrete made with

Limestone Screenings and with Torpedo Sand, F. B. Whitney, Thesis submitted to President and Faculty of Armour Institute of Technology, Chicago Illinois, 1905

12. Liberty Ships: Wikipedia.com: List of Liberty Ships, https://en.wikipedia.org/wiki/List_of_Liberty_ships_(A–F)

13 Tsunamis: Wikipedia.com: List of Tsunamis, https://en.wikipedia.org/wiki/List_of_tsunamis

14. NW Coast Earthquake History: "Cascadia subduction zone", Wikipedia. See Earthquake timing table of estimated year and interval

15. "13- year Cascadia study complete – and earthquake risk looms large", Oregon State University Newsroom, Source Chris Goldfinger, July 30, 2012

Appendix N: Data Use Authorizations

Authorizations for use of and limited contextual release of data from various sources follows. We thank all of the following agencies for their kind sharing of their data and for forthright authorizations. We thank all sources, including those not represented below, for their intellectual contributions.

Fonts for Paper Edition of this book- licensed for commercial use:

- General Text & Tables: Foulis Greek under SIL OFL License

- Chapter titles & subtitles: Josefin SANS SIL OFL License

- Python Produced Graphs: DejuVu SANS Freeware (Commercial Authorization)

- Spreadsheet Created Graphs: Either DejuVu SANS or Foulis Greek

Cover Art:

Book cover & web page images are Public Domain created by Gustave Dore' obtained from Dover Publications "The Dore' Bible Illustrations". Dover concurrence follows:

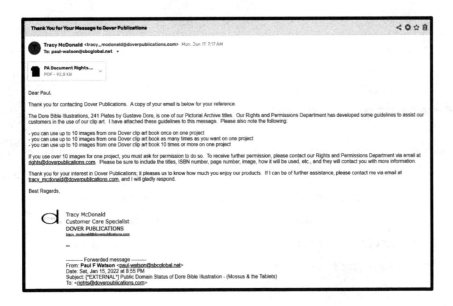

Australian Queensland Shark Research Program:

https://www.daf.qld.gov.au/business-priorities/fisheries/shark-control-program

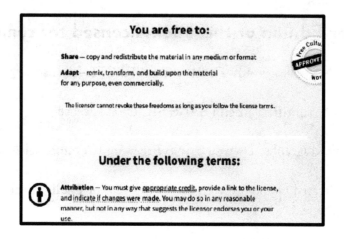

Japan Meteorological Society:

Japan Meteorological Agency Website Terms of Use: Information made available on the Japan Meteorological Agency website (hereafter referred to as "Content") may be freely used, copied, publicly transmitted, translated or otherwise modified on condition that the user complies with provisions 1) to 7) below. Commercial use of Content is also permitted. Note, however, that numerical data and data in simple tables, graphs, and so forth are not subject to copyright. Accordingly, the terms of use does not apply to such data, and said data may be used freely.

UN Food and Agriculture Organization of the United Nations:

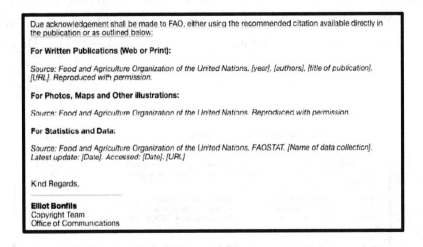

Due acknowledgement shall be made to FAO, either using the recommended citation available directly in the publication or as outlined below:

For Written Publications (Web or Print):

Source: Food and Agriculture Organization of the United Nations. [year], [authors], [title of publication]. [URL]. Reproduced with permission.

For Photos, Maps and Other illustrations:

Source: Food and Agriculture Organization of the United Nations. Reproduced with permission.

For Statistics and Data:

Source: Food and Agriculture Organization of the United Nations. FAOSTAT. [Name of data collection]. Latest update: [Date]. Accessed: [Date]. [URL]

Kind Regards,

Elliot Bonfils
Copyright Team
Office of Communications

NOAA US Government Agency

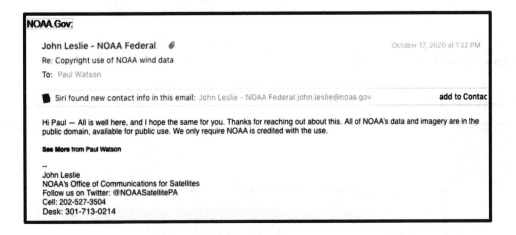

NOAA.Gov:

John Leslie - NOAA Federal   October 17, 2020 at 1:22 PM
Re: Copyright use of NOAA wind data
To: Paul Watson

Siri found new contact info in this email: John Leslie - NOAA Federal john.leslie@noaa.gov   add to Contac

Hi Paul — All is well here, and I hope the same for you. Thanks for reaching out about this. All of NOAA's data and imagery are in the public domain, available for public use. We only require NOAA is credited with the use.

See More from Paul Watson

--
John Leslie
NOAA's Office of Communications for Satellites
Follow us on Twitter: @NOAASatellitePA
Cell: 202-527-3504
Desk: 301-713-0214

Oregon and Washington Earthquake Data:

Material obtained from research reports and journal articles posted on the Internet. Fair use of factual data is claimed and sources of data are identified in footnotes.

USDA Data Authorization from USDA Website:

"Most information presented on the USDA Web site is considered public domain information. Public domain information may be freely distributed or copied, but use of appropriate byline/photo/image credits is requested. Attribution may be cited as follows: "U.S. Department of Agriculture."

US Government CDC Data:

Materials should be credited (e.g. "Source: CDC; "Statistics Developed by CDC". See www.cdc.gov

General and Factual Information:

Permissions reproduced above authorize most of the information used as a basis for statistical examples and explanations. A small amount of information was extracted from Journal articles, Internet Sources or published works and is footnoted in various chapters. Use of such material has been credited and is in accordance with accepted practices of fair use. Throughout creation of this work, it was always my wish to obtain permission, even when legality of use was clear.

"Fair Use" doctrine under copyright law was addressed by a Wikipedia Article entitled "Fair Use". From Wikipedia, "Facts and ideas are not protected by copyright law." This book makes widespread use of factual information (primarily tabular data) and such data has been referenced to its source. The author extends his thanks to the many individuals who have created source material.

Public Domain information can often be identified by creation date when it can be established. Where dates leave question, Internet searches were performed to establish public domain status, and to replace material as needed.

While every effort has been expended to credit the many people who have created resources used herein, your forbearance is requested if I have failed to give due credit. Please address any concerns to the author at the publisher address.

Omissions?

A genuine effort has been made to footnote sources of information and obtain permissions even when not strictly required. If you feel information was not credited to you that should have been, please e-mail paul-watson@sbcglobal.net so that I can address the situation. In the future, I will post additional credits (if any) at https://www.weibullbible.com

Appendix O: Bibliography

Weibull and Statistical Technical References & Sources of Statistical Data:

1. Computer Studies: were performed using Python 2.7, a public domain interpretative language. Some studies were made with Python 3 and others with Pythonista using iPad.

2. Computer Weibull Analysis Examples: Performed using Watson-Weibull Program owned and created by Paul Watson

3. Computer Weibull Analysis Examples: Performed using Weibull-DR, with permission of John Berner of Applications Research, Inc.

3. Spreadsheet analysis & graphs primarily created with NeoOffice Professional Edition 2017 for Mac

4. itl.nist.gov web site, for Failure and Hazard rate equations.

5. Mechanical Reliability, A.D.S. Carter, Bsc, C Eng. FI Mech E, FR AeS, John Wiley & Sons, NY 1972

6. Mechanical Survival, J. H. Bompas-Smith, Edited by R.H.W. Brook, London, 1973

7. Median Rank Calculation or Fractional Failures, HBM Presicia Inc., https://www.weibull.com/hotwire/issue187/hottopics187.htm, 2016

8. The New Weibull Handbook, by Robert B. Abernethy PhD, North Palm Beach Florida, 1993

9. Real Statistics Using Excel, Charles Zaiontz PhD, https://www.real-statistics.com/other-key-distributions/weibull-distribution/

10. Schaum's Statistics, Murray R. Spiegel PhD, New York, 1961

11. Used Math, Clifford E. Swartz, Englewood Cliffs, New Jersey, 1973

12. The Use of Weibull in Defect Data Analysis, Warwick Manufacturing Group 6 December, https"//warwick.ac.uk ...., 2004

13. Weibull Analysis Handbook, AFWAL-TR-83-2073 from Wright Patterson Aeronautical Laboratories, Final Report 1983

14. Wikipedia On-Line Encyclopedia: en.wikipedia.org, "Entropy" and other relevant articles.

15. The Japan Meteorological Agency https://www.jma.go.jp/jma/indexe.html

16. Journal of the United States Artillery, 1892 through 1903

17. Seacoast Fortifications of the United States by Emanuel Raymond Lewis 1970

18. British Battleships 1889-1904 by R. A. Burt 1998

19. Websites of the U.S. Government including USDA, CDC and Social Security.

20. Websites of the United Nations related to agricultural data

21. Various other web sites too numerous to recall for background information of various types.

Thank You-

I thank you for sharing your mind with me as you walked through various statistical concepts. Statistical studies are unavoidably tedious, but I hope you found something worthwhile that can help you in the future.

Paul F. Watson

CPSIA information can be obtained
at www.ICGtesting.com
Printed in the USA
JSHW052035210623
43503JS00002B/6